BY THE SAME AUTHOR

CONSTABLE
AROUND THE GREEN

Constable
Around the Green

NICHOLAS RHEA

ROBERT HALE · LONDON

ISBN 0 7090 5009 7

Robert Hale Limited
Clerkenwell House
Clerkenwell Green
London EC1R 0HT

Photoset in Plantin by
Derek Doyle & Associates, Mold, Clwyd.
Printed in Great Britain by
St Edmundsbury Press Ltd, Bury St Edmunds, Suffolk.
Bound by WBC Bookbinders Ltd, Bridgend, Mid-Glamorgan.

Contents

1 Games Upon the Green

As some divinely gifted man,
Whose life in low estate began
On a simple village green
Alfred, Lord Tennyson (1809–92)

Our poets have, on surprisingly few occasions, referred to the village green and, oddly enough, many of their references to this blissful area associate it with the playing of children. Robert Southey (1774–1843) does so in these lines:

It was a summer evening,
Old Kaspar's work was done,
And he before his cottage door,
Was sitting in the sun.
And by him sported on the green,
His little grandchild Wilhelmine.

William Blake (1757–1827) also featured youngsters when he wrote about the voices of children heard on the green. As a place of safety for children to play, the village green seemed perfect and it is not surprising that games like rounders, leap-frog, cricket and tig were played there and that the open space was used for the village fair, maypole dancing and other communal activities. Because the parents' homes were often clustered around the green, the children could be supervised.

There is of course, the archetypal village green. This is a flat, well-tended patch of lush grass of indeterminate size in the centre of the village. Around it are the most important buildings of the community – the church, the rectory, the inn, the manor-house, the shop and an array of delightfully rural cottages, probably with thatched roofs. On the green itself there may be some old stocks and an equally old pillory, a market cross or war memorial, a well, a maypole and even a pitch for playing cricket, football, bowls, rounders or quoits, plus a rippling stream nearby or a pond with ducks.

One vital element of a village green is that it is common land and therefore freely available to all, but in fact the nation's greens do vary enormously in shape, size and usage. A tour of the splendid English countryside will reveal the variety of our greens, and those on the North York Moors are no exception. Here, in villages like Goathland, Lealholm or Hutton-le-Hole you will find enormous stretches of undulating grass shorn smooth by the steady munching of free-range blackfaced sheep, but sadly some of the existing greens are now utilized as weekend car parks. Children of the visiting hordes now play between rows of parked vehicles while their parents snooze in the summer sun and leave behind their plastic litter and empty beer cans for the villagers to remove before the following weekend's onslaught. Sadly, the children of the local residents are compelled to go elsewhere for their own recreation and amusement.

In the dales, the greens are perhaps smaller than those of the more elevated moorland villages. Although some are not much larger than football fields, they do serve a similar communal purpose. But not every village boasts a green – indeed, in today's motorized society, many villages quietly congratulate themselves for not being blessed with a village green.

In these days of mass rural visiting, those villages without greens consider themselves fortunate because there is nowhere for the hordes to stop; those with village greens now suffer an awful loss of privacy from Easter until the end of October, the only compensation being that the influx of people does generate wealth for some of the more enterprising villagers and so keeps the rural economy viable. The greens of many pretty villages are therefore still being used by the public, albeit not by the residents, and this is done in a far less cheerful manner than in the past. Some visitors are very rude and intolerant of the residents' need to go about their daily lives and work, somehow oblivious to the fact that people actually live and work in such beautiful surroundings.

Happily, however, there are still a few quiet communities well off the proverbial beaten track in which the village green exists as it did in former times, and in which it continues its former role. One of those places is Slemmington which lies just off the southern edge of the North York Moors between Ashfordly and Eltering. Its green has all the features of a typical picture postcard setting.

The church with its tower and superb lychgate overlooks the green and all around are pretty stone cottages with red pantile roofs; a quiet stream flows through the village and it boasts mallard, teal and even swans in addition to its grayling and minnows. There is an ancient stone cross in the centre of the green and not far away, a set of stocks which were last used less than a century ago. There is a wishing-well with a dated cupola and, at the side of the green furthest from the stream, there is a pond which also attracts a variety of ducks, swans and wild water-fowl such as moorhens and coot.

There is an ancient ford across the stream too, but one curious factor concerns the stream. Here it is called Slemmington Beck, while two miles upstream, it is Gelderslack Beck and even higher, it is Shelvingby Beck. It changes its name to take on the identity of every village through which it passes before entering the River Rye near Malton and thus this single stream has a dozen different names.

But by far the most famous of Slemmington's attributes can also be seen on the green – it is the gigantic maypole which stands in its concrete base like a massive, slim and multicoloured tower. It is one of the tallest maypoles in the region, rising to some 72 feet in height and tapering towards the top. The tip bears a beautiful weather-vane in the form of a running fox; this splendid piece of metalwork is a present from a former blacksmith. The figure of the fox is re-gilded from time to time to keep it in pristine condition.

Painted in a range of bright colours, the maypole has been renewed several times dues to the effects of weather, use and age, and the present one dates to 1987, being a gift to the village from Lord Ashfordly's estate.

Each May Day, the village children dance around the pole having been trained since before Easter by their enthusiastic schoolteacher; the boys wear white shirts and red shorts, while the girls wear white dresses with red sleeves and collars. All wear white socks and black shoes. Their well-rehearsed repertoire of maypole dances is a charming sight and their display attracts an audience from near and far. Early in March every year, the maypole is lowered and repainted in readiness for the new season and once the pole has been re-positioned in April, the children begin their practising.

I used to enjoy my visits to Slemmington for it was always such a peaceful and friendly place with little or no crime. But the village became the scene of some curious criminal activity. Every time my patrolling took me through the village, I was reminded of that dramatic interlude; it happened shortly after I became the village constable at Aidensfield.

One bright sunny morning in early March, my telephone rang. I was seated at my desk in the office adjoining my police house and was typing a report about a minor traffic accident. I wondered who was calling at this time of morning, for it was only 8.30 a.m. I was slightly annoyed because I had wanted an early start in order to conclude some paper work.

'Jack Lawson.' I recognized the voice at the other end of the phone. He was clerk to Slemmington Parish Council.

'Morning, Jack,' I greeted him. 'What can I do for you this bright and sunny day?'

'It's our maypole, Mr Rhea, it's gone.'

'Gone?' I responded. 'Where's it gone?'

'Search me, but I think somebody's nicked it.'

'Nicked it? Who would want to steal a maypole?' I asked.

'There was a lot of good wood in it, it would make a useful pile of logs, Mr Rhea.'

'But if anybody tried to cut it up and sell it for firewood, it would be recognized immediately, it was all red, white, blue, yellow and green paint,' I retorted.

'Exactly, Mr Rhea. Fresh paint an' all. We'd just painted it for the bairns, to encourage them to practise their dancing. They'll be right upset and it'll take ages to find another, maypoles don't grow on trees, you know. Anyroad, I must report it, it belongs to the whole village. I just hope you fellers can help us get it back.'

'I'll come straight away,' I promised him.

Jack also ran the village store and post office and when I arrived, his first action was to show me the empty socket on the village green. I could see wheelmarks in the soft turf; a large vehicle of some kind had obviously been used. It would be impossible to hoist the huge and weighty pole from its deep socket by manpower alone; lifting gear would have been used.

'It's been lifted clean out of there,' he pointed to the empty hole. 'Now, to shift a thing that size needs muscle, and not human muscle. Mechanical muscle, Mr Rhea, like a bloody crane or summat with a grab or lifting gear.'

'What's it worth?' I put to him.

'Worth? Well, I mean, I can't put value on it, can you? You can't value a maypole.'

'But as firewood, Jack? As logs?'

'Well, you'd only get seventy or more logs out of it, that's not a lot, not a wagon-load by any means. So chopped into logs, I reckon I'd do well to get a couple of quid.'

'Thanks,' I said, pointing out that no one in their right mind would hire or use a huge vehicle of the kind that had been so obviously necessary to move it, merely to chop up the pole to earn themselves a couple of pounds. It did not make economic sense and thieves usually stole because they wanted to make an easy profit. This theft did not seem to fit into that category and I wondered if there was some other motive. I also found myself wondering if Claude Jeremiah Greengrass was behind this crime – stealing a maypole was the sort of daft thing he would do, although I did doubt whether even he had access to the necessary lifting gear.

I examined the surrounding green for further evidence. I drew a rough diagram of the large tyre tread marks in the hope I might be able to make some plaster casts of the tracks before they deteriorated, but there was nothing else of use to me.

I interviewed Jack in his kitchen over a cup of tea and a scone and obtained the necessary statement for my crime report. It included facts such as the last time it had been seen and the time it had been missed, together with a nominal value

and a note saying that no one had any authority to remove it.
Next I made a search of the village and began my enquiries. I
asked if anyone had heard or seen anything odd during the
night, but no one had. So far as my search was concerned,
there were not many places to conceal a 72-foot-long
multicoloured maypole, but if I did not search, Sergeant
Blaketon would ask why I hadn't done so. Thus I searched
behind all the local hedgerows, in the timber yards, along the
banks of the stream and every other likely place. I even
plodded through a copse of pine trees on the outskirts,
thinking that the maypole might have been hidden upright
among them. Then in all honesty, I could report a careful
search of the vicinity. I knew what Sergeant Blaketon would
think – he would think it was not a theft but a prank of some
kind. To be honest, I was still unsure myself; I needed either
to find the pole or to find a motive for the theft. But whether it
was a theft or a prank, or even a publicity stunt of some kind,
it was unfair to the children. I found myself dearly wishing I
could find it so that the children's rehearsals were not unduly
disrupted. I returned to Jack's shop and told him what I had
done, saying I would circulate details to all surrounding police
officers and would keep him informed of any progress.

'Should I try to find a new one?' he asked, worried about the
consequences if there was no maypole dancing this year.

'Let's give it a day or two,' I said, more in hope than in
realism. 'If it is a joke, it'll turn up somewhere. Those who
moved it won't want to disappoint the children.'

'I've called an emergency meeting of the parish council
tonight,' he said. 'I've invited the May Day committee too.
What can I tell them?'

'Tell them the matter is in the hands of the police,' I
suggested. 'You could ask everyone to keep their eyes open for
it and to help us find it. You might tell the local papers, there's
a good tale for them in this, and the publicity might just help.'

'It might persuade the thieves to cut it up an' all,' he
worried. 'But, Mr Rhea, where can you hide a maypole?'

'I don't know.' I sympathized with him in his moments of
agony and promised my very best efforts to recover it. My first
enquiry would be to Claude Jeremiah Greengrass.

When I walked into his untidy yard, Claude Jeremiah was busy sawing wood and, at my approach, his scruffy dog, Alfred, loped away into hiding; at first, I regarded that as a dual ominous sign but quickly saw that the timber was a pile of old railway sleepers and not the maypole. Alfred the lurcher, I felt, had an instinctive desire to hide from police officers, perhaps due to his breeding or else because of his dubious partnership in various illicit poaching expeditions.

As Alfred scrutinized me from an outbuilding with his hairy grey face poking through a gap in the rotting woodwork, Claude Jeremiah was reducing the sleepers to bundles of kindling which he'd sell around the district. He did not see or hear my approach due to his noisy actions and this gave me a brief opportunity to look around his buildings for signs of the maypole. But there was none.

'Morning, Claude,' I shouted above the noise of his saw.

He stopped work. His face dropped when he saw me standing behind him and said, 'It wasn't me, Mr Rhea, definitely not me.'

'What wasn't you?' I asked.

'Whatever you're here for, whatever's happened, it wasn't me. I didn't do it.'

'What have you done with the Slemmington maypole?' I decided to pull his leg a little, a way of getting my own back for the hassle he caused me from time to time.

'Me? I've done nowt with any maypole, Mr Rhea.'

'Not even chopped it up for firewood?' I eyed his pile of cut timber.

'Railway sleepers, Mr Rhea, all creosoted, a job lot, they're closing lines and selling 'em off cheap. They make real good kindling.'

'I believe you, many wouldn't,' I laughed and then began to walk around his rubbish-cluttered premises, lifting lids off bins, moving old tyres and peering into sheds.

Alfred emerged and slunk into a position of safety behind his master and the pair of them followed me around with Claude Jeremiah explaining where he had obtained the objects of my pretended interest. Finally I stopped.

'Someone's stolen the Slemmington maypole,' I told him.

'Sometime during the night. We want it back for the kids, Claude, so if you come across it during your travels, let us know, eh?'

'Right you are, Mr Rhea, yes, I'll keep my ears open. A maypole, eh? Now there's a thing. Fancy pinching a maypole.'

'My sentiments exactly, Claude. Who on earth would do that?'

Claude Jeremiah scratched his head and pretended to think deeply. 'Somebody with a use for one, I reckon, Mr Rhea,' he grinned. 'And not many folks have any use for a maypole these days, either new or second-hand.'

'So in your opinion, there's not a big market for second-hand maypoles, Claude?'

'Definitely not, Mr Rhea.'

'But if there was, you might be tempted?' I watched him with interest.

'Now then, Mr Rhea, that's putting ideas where there was none. No, I'd never pinch a maypole; well, I mean, I'd never get it out of the ground, would I? I'd need heavy lifting gear which I haven't got.'

'You could always steal a crane, Claude. Or borrow one. Now, somebody's got it out of the ground and spirited the thing away. Even I reckon that's beyond you, so I won't keep you away from your honest labours any longer.'

And I left man and dog to continue their chores. My next journey was to Ashfordly police station where I had to formally record the crime and to circulate it in our various publications. But Sergeant Blaketon was not at all pleased.

'You're not serious, Rhea?' he bristled. 'Who'd pinch a maypole? It'll have been taken down for redecorating or whatever they do. Maintenance. Repairs.'

'No, Sergeant,' I said. 'That's all been done. It had just undergone its annual service and had been reinstated, all new and shining bright. Then it was spirited away during the hours of darkness, sometime between nine o'clock last night and eight o'clock this morning.'

'There's no market for stolen maypoles, Rhea, not like jewellery and antiques . . . .'

'It's not even an antique maypole, Sergeant,' I couldn't

resist that retort. 'I can't see any antique dealer buying it.'

'I can't see anybody in their right minds taking it, Rhea. Are you sure it's been stolen? This isn't a prank of some kind is it? Somebody preparing for April Fool's Day? A stunt of some sort?'

I explained that I had considered all those possibilities and after making enquiries from the local people, plus a search of all likely maypole hiding-places and an interview with Claude Jeremiah Greengrass, I had to conclude that it was a genuine crime. This meant it would become part of our crime statistics, and if we didn't trace the thief, it would become part of our 'unsolved crime' figures. It would look as if there was a crime wave in Slemmington.

'It won't look good in our crime stats. and monthly returns, Rhea,' worried Sergeant Blaketon.

'Then we'll have to trace the culprit,' I said. 'How about writing me off normal duties to concentrate on detecting this heinous crime?' I suggested.

'Don't be so bloody daft, Rhea,' was all he said.

The inspector at Eltering, the superintendent at divisional headquarters and the detective superintendent at force headquarters, all queried the crime; each thought the maypole's disappearance was nothing but a prank. In spite of their reservations, however, a genuine crime report had been made and so the fate of the Slemmington maypole became part of our official crime statistics.

I returned to Slemmington later that day to continue my enquiries, the only development coming from a young mother who'd been awake at night tending her crying baby. Around 2 a.m., she'd heard the noise of a heavy vehicle moving slowly through the village, but hadn't looked out to see what it was.

If she had, I reckon she'd have noticed the removal of the said stolen property.

Three days passed without any useful maypole-detecting information coming into my possession. Slemmington Parish Council was growing increasingly concerned about my lack of results and were putting pressure on Jack Lawson to obtain a replacement. Meanwhile, the local weekly paper had not yet been published and so wider publicity among the public had not yet been achieved. It was a harrowing time for all.

And then the following day, as in all good detective stories, a piece of timely good fortune came my way. Living in a large converted farmhouse on the edge of the moors near Lairsbeck was a retired military gentleman who rejoiced in the name of Colonel Cuthbert Cruikshank-Carstairs. Three days after the maypole vanished, I had to visit him about the renewal of his firearms certificate and, as always, he welcomed me into his spacious, book-lined study while his wife brewed some strong coffee from home-ground beans. Colonel Cuthbert, as everyone called him, was an authority on country life; he wrote books and articles for magazines like *The Field* and *Country Life* and lectured to organizations ranging from the Women's Institute to adult educational courses about all aspects of rural living. His expertise ranged from fox hunting to folk lore by way of local customs, rural superstitions and ancient herbal cures.

Knowledgeable about all kinds of wildlife from fish to flowers, birds to bees and ferrets to foxes, he was a veritable treasure-house of country knowledge. Having completed the business of my visit, we chatted over our coffee and he asked me what was happening in the constabulary world beyond his village. I told him about the maypole theft and he smiled.

'Revenge,' he beamed. 'That will be Waindale getting their own back.'

'Waindale?' I must have sounded puzzled because he laughed at my reaction.

'You've not heard about the feud?' he asked.

'No,' I had to admit, wondering why, if there was a feud between Waindale and Slemmington, Jack Lawson hadn't told me.

'Years ago,' he said, 'Waindale had a lovely maypole, the tallest in this area. The villagers held a May Day festival every year and there is little doubt it was the finest display for miles around. The other villages were jealous, some tried to compete by arranging their own maypole dancing but none could match Waindale's dancing and none could produce a maypole of such impressive height. But of all the competing villages, Slemmington almost succeeded. Lord Ashfordly donated

them a fine pole from his woods, it was not quite as tall as
Waindale's but it was a very fine specimen. The acquisition of
a fine pole encouraged Slemmington to recruit and train its
own fine troup of dancers led by a lovely maiden called
Susanna Browning.

'But the trainer of the Waindale group got his eye on her.
He wooed her and wed her, thus taking away Slemmington's
leading dancer. Well, no one could forgive Waindale for that
act of piracy and so, the next thing that happened was that
Waindale's fine maypole vanished over night. Miraculously, at
that very same time, Slemmington acquired a very tall one, far
taller than any of its earlier specimens. The suspicions were
always there, rumours abounded. It was said that if
Slemmington couldn't have Susanna, they would have the
finest maypole. There is no doubt that the Waindale-ites
believed Slemmington had purloined their pole, but the
Slemmingtonians have always denied they were criminals.'

'When was this?' I asked.

'March 1766,' he told me. 'In March 1866, Slemmington
was raided overnight and its maypole was stolen. A similar one
was found in Waindale, but no one could prove it was the
same pole. Sadly, Waindale's maypole ceremonies never
maintained their earlier attraction and, in 1907, they ended.
Waindale has never had a maypole, or a maypole ceremony,
since that time. In contradiction, Slemmington's ceremony
has flourished.'

'And now,' I said. 'It is March 1966, two hundred years
since the feud started.'

'Exactly,' beamed Colonel Cuthbert. 'The anniversary of
the original battle. So it would not surprise me that if you were
to pay a visit to Waindale, you might find a handsome maypole
sitting in the old socket . . . .'

'I was there early last week,' I said. 'There was no maypole
on the green then.'

'Precisely,' he said.

I thanked him and after leaving his comfortable house,
drove through the winding lanes and across the windswept
moors to Waindale. This is a tiny community comprising a
few stone cottages and a couple of farms around the village

green, but there is no inn, no post office, no shop and no church. Its only feature is a telephone kiosk, although there is a timber-yard on the outskirts. There was rarely any reason for me to visit Waindale but now, as I drove in, I could see the enormous maypole which dominated the skyline.

It was rooted firmly into the old concrete-surrounded socket. To my inexpert eye, it looked identical to the one which had vanished from Slemmington but to my official police officer's eye, I knew there was no way of proving, to the satisfaction of a court of law, that this was that very same pole. As I studied the mighty edifice, I noticed that the top bore the metal carving of a team of shire horses drawing a wagon. That type of wagon is known as a wain in this area; wagons were once constructed here and the village was rich with skilled wainwrights, hence the name Waindale. A local farmer, Robin Hartree, noticed my interest and wandered across.

'Now then, Mr Rhea,' he smiled. 'Two quick visits, eh? It's not often we see you hereabouts on such a regular basis.'

'It's not often I need to come,' I said. 'I only come like this every hundred years or so when somebody decides to pinch a maypole.'

'Ours is safe enough,' and his eyes twinkled. 'Nobody's pinched ours.'

'But somebody's pinched one from Slemmington,' I said.

'They got their famous big maypole by pinching it from us, Mr Rhea. They've always made do with second-hand maypoles.'

'And Waindale doesn't?'

'Nay, lad, ours are allus new 'uns, just look at that paint, glistening like new. We're reviving our old custom, in honour of Susanna Browning. You'll not know of Susanna Browning?' he grinned.

'But I do,' I said, telling him the story as told to me by Colonel Cuthbert. And when I finished, I told him that I knew all about the story of the oft-stolen maypoles, adding that it might just be a coincidence that there was a timber-yard on the edge of Waindale, a business belonging to a man from Waindale which had all the gear necessary for lifting tree-trunks from the woods and maypoles from their sockets.

'Well, Mr Rhea,' he said. 'I'd say Waindale has only got what's rightly theirs, and that doesn't mean I'm saying this pole came from Slemmington.'

If indeed this was the Slemmington pole, then it did not rightly belong to Waindale because this particular pole had been a recent gift to Slemmington from Lord Ashfordly.

Even so, I did have some sympathy with the Waindale folk who were, even after the passage of two centuries, still smarting over their lost maypole.

When I returned to see Jack Lawson, he launched immediately into a tirade of anger without waiting to hear my news. He said he was furious because during the night someone had left the village's metal fox, minus the maypole, on his front doorstep and this piece of cheek had been aggravated because he had managed to find a replacement pole, but it was a mere 36 feet tall instead of 72 feet – only half the size of the missing one.

'Calm down, Jack,' I said. 'I think I've found your missing pole,' and I told him of my discoveries, not forgetting the story of Susanna Browning.

'I never thought anybody would remember that anniversary,' he said. 'I mean, I read about it when I was a lad, in an old local history book, but it's never been mentioned for generations. To be honest, we don't pay much attention to it in this village, it happened two hundred years ago so it's really got nothing to do with us now. Anyway, Waindale's got our maypole, so when do we get it back?'

'I can't prove it's yours, Jack,' and I explained the legal difficulties. 'All I can say is that there is a pole which matches yours exactly, and it is standing on Waindale village green.'

'But it is ours, Mr Rhea!'

'I know that and you know that, but there's no way to prove it if Waindale deny they removed it. Now listen, if someone was to remove that pole and replace it on Slemmington green, then put the smaller one in its place, I'd say the same logic would apply. One pole is just like another . . . .'

'Are you saying no questions would be asked?'

'I'm saying it would be difficult to distinguish one brightly painted maypole from another, especially one with a fox on top . . . .'

'I'll make a fuss about erecting our new one,' he grinned.
'That'll mislead Waindale . . . I'll have words with our
Maypole Action Committee. When's your night off, Mr
Rhea?'

'Friday,' I said.

On Saturday morning, I made a point of touring
Slemmington and noticed the tall, gleaming maypole with the
fox on top. It was in position on the green and a small
committee of men were admiring it. I stopped and Jack came
over to me.

'We've got a nice new pole, Mr Rhea,' he grinned. 'Exactly
the same height and colour of the one we lost.'

'That's amazing,' I said. 'I trust you've anchored it well into
its base?'

'We have,' he said. 'Concreted it in and we're erecting a
secondary structure around the base, like a flagpole has, to
give it added security. You and Mrs Rhea will be coming to
our May Day ceremonies?'

'I might look in,' I said. 'Well, I must be off. I thought I
might have a look at Waindale's new maypole.'

'They tell me they've got a good 'un, Mr Rhea, but not
quite as tall as ours.'

I smiled as I drove away. Waindale did indeed have a fine
maypole and it was considerably smaller than the one I'd seen
there earlier. Robin Hartree saw me examining it and came
across for a word.

'Someone's given us a nice new maypole, Mr Rhea,' he
smiled.

'Someone must love Susanna Browning,' I countered.
'You'll be celebrating May Day perhaps?'

'Now we've got a maypole of our own, we might just do
that,' he said. 'But none of us here knows owt about maypole
dancing, Mr Rhea; we need someone to show us how to cope
with all those ribbons and things.'

'There's some very knowledgeable folk in Slemmington,' I
said. 'They've some maypole experts there, I'm told, quite
friendly folk they are, when you get to know them.'

Each village was therefore quite happy with the outcome of
the great maypole mystery and each village now stages its own

maypole ceremonies. The feuding has been suspended until 2066, but the lack of positive and legally acceptable identification of each pole meant the police could never be sure that the precise pole that was stolen had ever been replaced.

Replacement by a substitute meant that the original was still recorded as missing and because of that, the crime is still listed as 'undetected'.

The next piece of villainy in Slemmington's crime wave also occurred on the village green. It involved the scorer for the cricket team which was known throughout the district as The Chadwicks. The Chadwicks was Slemmington's village team, but the entire team comprised men with that surname – brothers, cousins, fathers, sons, grandfathers and uncles. The team had been playing for years, always comprised entirely of Chadwicks; even the reserves were called Chadwick so it required a scorer with more than average acumen to keep track of their runs, wickets, bowling and resultant analyses.

Such a man was Cyril Pulling, a bespectacled and meticulous clerk who worked in the accounts office of a nearby animal feeds production company. Small, neat and extremely tidy, Cyril was married with an equally neat and tidy wife and two equally neat and tidy children. The house was small and neat and the family ran a small and neat Morris mini car.

Cyril's Saturdays during the summer consisted of scoring for The Chadwicks and he drove to all their matches in his immaculate little car. It was always polished and gleaming; in spite of having two small children, Cyril's car was never full of childish things like sweet papers, toys and games, neither were its windows greasy with finger marks.

Cyril was a serious fellow; he tackled his scoring duties with the same commitment as his company results or his own income tax returns, but he never seemed to smile. Those who knew him realized that this was his means of enjoying himself, of getting himself out of the office. Even if it meant working with columns of figures, Cyril regarded it as a holiday and therefore a welcome break. Scoring for The Chadwicks was his relaxation.

Unfortunately, his serious nature often meant he was a butt

for jokes and one Saturday, when he parked his beautiful car behind the pavilion at the edge of Slemmington's village green, he left the doors open and the key in the ignition switch. The temptation was too much for three of the village lads. Whilst the first half of the match was in progress, they pushed the little car onto the lane and down the gentle slope, then drove it into an old barn just across the narrow bridge and closed the barn doors. This was their idea of a joke; they never thought for a moment that their prank would be considered theft of a motor vehicle.

Cyril noticed its absence during the break when he went for his sandwiches and flask; realizing he had left his key with the car, he knew he had been foolish and that someone was now driving around in his pride and joy. Cyril knew precisely what to do when a crime was committed and so, without wasting a moment, he dialled 999.

I was on patrol between Ashfordly and Eltering that afternoon and when I received the call on my radio, I diverted to the cricket ground and arrived within ten minutes. Play had not resumed so I was able to talk to Cyril; I doubt if he would have abandoned his scoring just to talk to me had I arrived after the recommencement of play. I had the registration number – that had been circulated after his 999 call – but I needed more detail and listened as he explained about parking it. As we chatted, I noticed three youths hanging around and watching my activities, but did not regard their interest as unusual or significant. When play resumed, I decided to search the vicinity for the car – we always searched the area when a crime had been reported. I began by driving along the lane.

Very quickly, I spotted the wheelmarks in the soft grass and the three sets of footprints, one at the steering-wheel side and two to the rear . . . .

Equally quickly, I saw the flattened grass at the entrance to the old barn. It had been depressed by the opening and closing of the huge doors; I could also see the twin tracks leading inside. It was the work of a moment to find the car.

As I hauled open the heavy doors, I became aware of the presence of those three youths, all about sixteen and all watching me from behind the shelter of a thick hedgerow. They thought I could not see them . . . . Either they had hidden the car as a prank, or else it had been concealed here to be collected later by the thieves or perhaps a receiver.

Either way, I could deal with the matter. I radioed Control and requested that Scenes of Crime be informed, asking them to attend to examine the car for fingerprints and other evidence. The good news was that the Scenes of Crime vehicle was in the vicinity, having just attended an office-break-in in Strensford. It would arrive within a matter of minutes.

I closed the barn doors to await their arrival, thus securing the car. In the absence of a lock on the barn, I parked the police van in front of the doors and locked it, then returned on foot to the village green. I went into the pavilion and waited for the over to finish before informing Cyril of my discovery. He was delighted; I said the car did not appear to be damaged but that our Scenes of Crime people were en route and the car would be restored to him once they had concluded their investigation. I then said I suspected a prank by the three youths who, by now, were outside the pavilion watching me chat to Cyril. From their demeanour, I thought they were plucking up courage to talk to me.

I went out to them.

'What do you lads know about Cyril's car?' I looked at each in turn. Three frightened faces peered at me, so I decided to capitalize on this fear. 'If it's been stolen and if I find the culprits, they'll be in serious trouble. Our Scenes of Crime officers are on their way now, to examine the car for fingerprints . . . so let's suppose I asked for your fingerprints, all of you? I wonder what I'd find?'

'It was us, Mr Rhea,' said the taller one. 'But we didn't steal it, we just hid it, as a joke . . . honest.'

'Ah!' I peered down at them, trying to appear fierce. 'Well, it seems your joke has backfired, doesn't it? I have received a report that the car was stolen, and when you take someone's property without permission, that is stealing, especially when you hide it so the owner can't find it . . . .'

I was about to lecture them about dishonesty when SOCO, the name we gave to the Scenes of Crime Officers, eased on to he village green parking area in their marked vehicle. The boys' faces showed their dismay and one of them, whom I later discovered was called Andrew Staples, began to weep.

'I think you lads have learned a lesson,' I said. 'Now wait here. I'll have words with our officers, then I'll come back to you. Right?'

They waited, huddled in a sorry group as I went to speak to SOCO.

'Hello, Sarge,' I greeted Detective Sergeant Power.

'Stolen car, Nick?' he asked. 'Can you show us?'

'Sure, down here,' and I led the way back to the old barn, moved my police van and showed them the car.

'Right,' said Power. 'I'll fetch my troops.'

'Since calling you,' I said. 'I've found the culprits,' and I told him the story. He listened and smiled.

'I don't think we can crime this one, Nick,' he said. 'Can we have a word with the loser and ask him to withdraw his complaint? They're only kids, juveniles, and no court would convict them.'

'Suits me.' I was happy to go along with this. 'But I think we should teach those lads a lesson.'

'That's easy,' grinned Power. 'Let's have a word with the owner first.'

'He's scoring, we'll have to wait for a break in the game,' I said.

'That's fine,' said Power. 'There'll be a cup of tea around, I expect, and I like watching cricket anyway.'

Cyril Pulling listened to Sergeant Power's plan and actually smiled as he nodded his agreement. 'I'll agree to that,' he said. 'There's no damage to my car and no harm's been done.'

When Power had had three mugs of tea and umpteen scones and cakes made by the cricket teams' wives, we returned to Cyril's mini, eased it out of the garage and drove it back to the side of the cricket pitch. The three youths watched us with some apprehension. Then Sergeant Power and his two colleagues, both detective constables, set to work.

One was the official photographer, the other a Scenes of Crime officer and under the directions of the sergeant, they literally smothered the car in grey fingerprint powder. There was thick powder everywhere,

Within five minutes, that lovely little vehicle looked like something which had been stored in a dusty shed from the time that Adam was a lad.

'Right, you three,' shouted Sergeant Power before brushing the powder in his search for prints. 'Come here.'

The three youths came across, nervous and apprehensive.

'You took this car for a prank, right?'

'Yes, sir,' said Andrew Staples.

'Well, it needs cleaning, doesn't it? It needs to be as clean as it was before it got covered in all this powder. Now, I have cleaning materials in my van, plenty of dusters and so on, and so that's your job. Mr Pulling wants his car as clean as a new pin by the time the cricket match finishes. Right? And I'll remain here to make sure it is. Got it?'

'Yes, sir,' said the three chastened lads.

It was a good match. The Chadwicks won by a wicket and ten runs, each of the police officers present, including myself, had a grandstand view of the game aided by endless cups of tea and lots of scrumptious home-made food, while three hard-working lads made a superb job of polishing Cyril's car.

'It's cleaner than when I lost it,' said Cyril afterwards – and smiled again.

2 Fiends in High Places

There are no tricks in plain and simple faith.
William Shakespeare (1564–1616)

The practised confidence trickster is a curious mixture of evil
cunning and winsome appeal; by using this combination of
characteristics he or she may persuade others to part with
gifts, money, accommodation or even to permit use of the
so-called secret parts of their bodies. Over the centuries,
unscrupulous men have charmed their way into the beds of
gullible girls, scheming women have persuaded rich men to
marry them for better or for a lot worse, and there is a roaming
army of pestilent confidence tricksters who prey on old folks,
vicars, charity workers and others who are blessed with warm
hearts. This plague of wandering charlatans comprises villains
and parasites who live off the generosity of innocent victims in
their constant effort to feed and clothe themselves, often in
luxury. Con men have been known to charm hard-won
life-savings from poor pensioners, only to lose the lot in a
moment of high living or reckless gambling. There is
deep-seated cruelty in people who will do such evil things and
although some would admire their devious skills, the police
know their true worth and do their utmost to warn their
potential victims, to trap the rogues and to bring them to
justice.

But trapping such wily characters is like seizing an eel; no
matter how sure your grip, the eel will wriggle in its own slime
until it is free from your clutches – and confidence tricksters
are very similar. They are as slippery as the proverbial eel but
infinitely more cunning and nasty.

They rely upon their silver tongues and well-rehearsed charm to get them out of trouble. It is a sad truth that many of them do evade justice. They know how to use the letter of the law and the sympathy of their victims to their full advantage and in some cases, their charm is such that even the victims refuse to believe that their new 'friend' is a wrongdoer. In many cases, the victims do not wish to prosecute and while this protects that victim from the scorn of their neighbours, it leaves the villain free to prey on others.

In Yorkshire, we call such people 'slape tongued', which means slippery tongued; I believe it was the Red Indians in cowboy films who called such people fork-tongued because a snake's tongue is often forked – and who can trust a snake? God made the serpent the lowest of the low, a beast destined to crawl for ever on its belly, and this is an apt comparison with the guile of a confidence trickster. They are among the lowest of humanity's low and I believe there is a famous quotation, whose origin escapes me, which says 'There is no heart below the head of a serpent'.

The famous nineteenth-century criminologist, Dr Hans Gross, had a lot to say about confidence tricksters too – in one paragraph he describes them as 'generally men who have received a good education in their youth, or who at least have had the opportunities of picking up the appearance of such. Without exception, they are men of ability, full of dexterity and presence of mind, but with a love of easy and idle life'.

He offers a picture of a typical fraudster and it is perhaps worthy of inclusion here.

> Fashionably dressed, he steps into a jeweller's shop and steals while pretending to select, or he causes the valuable selected to be brought to his hotel, takes delivery and disappears through another door; he goes to the banker and collects the amount of a forged cheque; he manages to get introduced to the highest social circles, runs up heavy debts and disappears; he cheats at play and that on a large scale; he becomes engaged to one or more wealthy young ladies and makes off with money borrowed from presumptive fathers-in-law; he buys houses and estates without paying for them, mortgages them and

disappears; he gets into business relations with a merchant and runs up debts in his name; in a word, he knows marvellously well how to play upon that weakness in mankind that allows itself to be bluffed by a high-sounding name, fine clothes, and easy and self-possessed manners; he knows there are fools to be found always and everywhere, and lives at their expense until he is caught.

Whilst a constable at Aidensfield, I was often in receipt of police circulars which warned of tricksters on the move. In such cases, we would then warn any potential victims who lived and worked on our beats. Bed-and-breakfast establishments were commonly targeted by travelling con men who slept and ate, then left without paying, and so we would tour those on our respective patches to alert them. Some confidence tricksters would specialize in visiting vicarages where they told a sorrowful and harrowing tale of some kind, following which the vicar gave them tea, sympathy, a pocket full of money and sometimes a bed for the night. Off would go the fraudster to another vicarage where he would repeat the yarn and the sneaky side of such acts often remained unknown until one clergyman chanced to be talking to another about their daily work and compared notes about helping the poor.

The tale that had been told so well to both was usually enough for the vicars to realize they had been well and truly tricked out of their hard-earned money; they would ring the police and we would circulate a description of the wanted villain, by which time, of course, he was usually miles away in another diocese doing exactly the same thing. No matter how widely we circulated his activities, he usually managed to select a vicar who hadn't been warned or who, if warned, did not believe that the charming fellow in his study was indeed the biblical wolf or false prophet in sheep's clothing.

In one case, a con man was actually arrested in our area and he had to be transported to the Midlands where he was wanted for serious offences in the Birmingham area. He was taken to Birmingham by train, being handcuffed to a detective *en route*, but during the journey he even managed to persuade the detective to give him £5! He said he had no money but wanted to buy some flowers for his granny who would be most upset at his arrest. Of course, there was no upset granny . . . .

This incident shows that policemen are human too, and that some of us can be persuaded to believe the sorrowful stories of a skilled confidence trickster. Of course, that sort of thing would never happen to me . . . .

Clever disguise was sometimes resorted to by confidence tricksters and a favourite was a clergyman's dog collar. This was one of the most simple to effect. If one is approached by a man in a dark suit and a back-to-front collar, then one is usually tempted to believe that he is trustworthy. As a consequence, there are many travelling rogues who dress up as priests or vicars, nuns or monks but perhaps the most interesting of the clerical con men within my knowledge was the one who came to Aidensfield to establish a monastery. To be honest, I am still not sure whether or not he was a genuine man of God with a desire to perpetuate his faith or whether he was a charlatan.

When the impressive figure of Father Severus Sanandaj, a priest from the Patriarchate of the Karakumian Branch of the Orthodox Adiaphoritic Apostolic Church arrived in Aidensfield, we all warmed to him in a spirit of ecumenical love, hope and joy. He was a majestic figure some six feet five inches tall, with long black hair aided by a heavy black beard and moustache. Underneath all that hair, his age was difficult to determine, but I guessed he was in his middle forties. He was a fit man who enjoyed physical activity; he walked miles and from time to time would disrobe and enjoy a hectic swim in the local swimming-baths.

During his daily routine, he wore the long, all-embracing black vestments of a priest of the Orthodox Church, the kind which can still be seen in Greece, and upon his head he wore a tall tubular black hat with a rim around the top. To see him, fully robed, walking down the main street of Aidensfield was indeed a memorable and remarkable sight.

He was a quiet man who seemed to be totally content with his religious life and he lived in a rented cottage along one of the quieter lanes of the village. I was never sure precisely when or how he arrived; he just seemed to materialize upon the village scene but with Maddleskirk Abbey only two miles away, the sight of a foreign priest, monk or nun in the area was not regarded as unusual. Many came from all over the world to Maddleskirk Abbey for retreats or spiritual renewal, or to attend conferences relating to church matters.

Thus Father Severus was regarded as just another foreign and interesting priest who had been drawn to this place of religious succour.

When I asked George in the pub if he knew about the Orthodox priest, George confirmed those thoughts by saying,

'He's summat to do with the abbey, Mr Rhea, he walks along there to see the monks, joins them in church and for meals and things. They're supporting him, he fled from the Soviet Union by all accounts, got away from the Communists and made his way across Europe to England. He's from some obscure branch of the Orthodox faith and reckons he's trying to keep his church alive. He wants to establish a small monastery in Aidensfield.'

It all made sense. The Roman Catholic monks of Maddleskirk Abbey did encourage those of other faiths to join them and I did know they were very active in keeping Christianity alive in various Communist countries. This man had undoubtedly contacted them when he was in dire need of help – and he had come to live amongst us, at least for a short time. I knew the villagers would make him most welcome.

Soon after his arrival, a caravan appeared in the garden of his cottage and within a week or so, it had sprouted something that looked like a huge onion with a leek standing beside it. The caravan was his church, the central point of his new monastery, and the onion-shaped thing was its dome; the leek beside the dome was a small decorative copy of a minaret.

Soon, the dome was painted with gold paint, the minaret was gilded in parts, and a splendid icon of the Virgin Mary appeared on the side of the caravan. The entire complex looked like a cross between a miniature Kremlin and model of Brighton's Royal Pavilion but when I saw what had appeared in that lane, I wondered from where he drew his congregation and how he intended to support himself. But such problems were no real concern of mine – I knew that many monastic establishments had had very modest beginnings and had survived through the faith of their founders and the devotion of their supporters. Perhaps the Orthodox Adiaphoritic Apostolic Church of Aidensfield would similarly flourish?

My duties and those of Father Severus never came into contact. From time to time, however, I did have to visit the administrative offices of Maddleskirk Abbey and sometimes found myself talking with the abbot. On one such occasion, I took the opportunity to refer to Father Severus and his onion.

I discovered that he was already well known in the abbey. The cottage he was using was owned by the abbey trustees; it was a spare house which could be used by guests to the abbey. One common use was for Anglican priests who had left their own church to become Catholics, but who needed a period for contemplation away from all religious influences. They would stay there to gather their thoughts; Catholic priests facing a crisis of faith would also use it, as would any other deserving person.

Father Severus, I was told, having fled from oppression and Communism, was one such deserving case. He lived there free of rent, his food was supplied by the abbey and he could join the brethren for lunch and evening meals whenever he wished. He was even given a small allowance of cash for his daily essentials, and had been allowed use of all the abbey's comprehensive facilities and contacts. Hence his caravan, onion and icon.

Neither I nor anyone else had cause to suspect he was not genuine. But, eventually, tiny hints began to appear. He took up swimming in the local baths where he presented a splendid figure and attracted the interest of many women, some of whom, I am sure, felt sorry for the celibate man and his onion. I do know that he took one or two ladies out for expensive meals.

Or perhaps they took him out? I never found out who paid the bills but I reckoned it might be either the abbey trustees or the ladies in question. On another occasion, he ordered a case of wine from The Brewer's Arms and told George to send the bill to the abbey. Later, I saw one or two ladies journeying individually to Aidensfield to attend his monastery and admire his minaret; once or twice, I saw well-dressed ladies emerging with a smile from his church and wondered if they had been on a pilgrimage or a therapeutic visit to the handsome priest.

Father Severus expanded his range of powerful physical activities, going for long, fast runs, swimming or playing rugby football with a local team.

He performed other feats of strength and endurance too, such as running a marathon and weight-lifting. He once joined some TA volunteers on an exercise involving abseiling, rock climbing and a fearsome assault course, and left a lot of the younger men breathless. In time, tales of his prowess became commonplace and there was no doubt that he was a strong and very fit man. Rugged, powerful and tough, he was not the conventional image of a man of God.

But as I received no complaints about his behaviour, I could not therefore take any specific action against him. Besides, his way of life was none of my business. If he was living off the generosity of the local abbey and some local lonely women, then was that wrong? Certainly, it was not wrong if they volunteered to support him as he came to terms with his exile, but was he using deceit and trickery to achieve those comforts? I must admit that I did have some anxieties about him, particularly as his use of English was so good.

Conscious of my duties towards the people of Aidensfield and district, I did try to find out a little more about the Karakumian Branch of the Orthodox Adiaphoritic Apostolic Church. But the more I delved into the complexities of the historic links between the Catholic and Orthodox churches, the more confusing it became. I did learn, however, that there had been a branch of the Eastern Orthodox Church whose followers were known as Monophysites; there was a breakaway group of this sect, and they were known as Adiaphorites.

And I did discover that towns called Karachev, Karakuny, Karakumskiy and Karakulimi did exist in various parts of the USSR. I also found out that one of the bishops of the Monophysitic Orthodox Church was called Severus. He was Bishop of Antioch in AD 513. Our chap had taken his name.

But having made these minor discoveries, I also knew that

the hallmark of a good con man was to establish what appeared to be an authentic base for his story. This man had done that – it would take a great deal of infinitely more detailed research to prove that his church did not exist and equally, because communication with the Soviet authorities was so difficult, it would probably be impossible to establish the bona fides of Father Severus. So who was he? Was he English? German? Russian? Hungarian? I had no idea.

In my policeman's mind, this man was a mystery and when I had a rendezvous with Sergeant Blaketon one morning, I decided to voice my concern. I told him about Father Severus and he listened intently.

'Have you had any complaints about him, Rhea?' he asked.

'No, Sergeant,' I had to admit. 'Not one.'

'Then it's no concern of ours, is it?'

'But if he is conning all those monks and those women, then he ought to be stopped. If they are being charitable because they think he's genuine when in fact he might be a rogue, then he's nothing more than a cunning and evil scrounger.'

'If one of them makes an official complaint, we can do something about it, but what's he done wrong, Rhea? There's nothing wrong in people being charitable! And well-meaning people do create new religions and churches. Jesus did it, didn't he?'

'Jesus got crucified because folks thought he was a villain,' I reminded Blaketon.

'There'll always be miscarriages of justice, Rhea, and I don't want one in the case of your Father Severus. If there's no formal complaint, it suggests he's done nothing wrong, and that means we can't – and shouldn't – take action. And he hasn't done anything wrong, has he?'

'He hasn't been found out, you mean,' I retorted.

'So he charms the ladies and persuades holy men to support him. Where's the criminality in that, Rhea? It's being done the world over, and has been for centuries.'

I realized I was not making any headway and decided to keep my ears and eyes open for any further hints about the background of Father Severus. I even paid a visit to his church, just to have a look inside, and he was charming and helpful, speaking in good English with what appeared to be a strong Eastern European accent. He showed me into the caravan with its small altar, its icons and its ornate gold leaf decor. Before the altar stood half a dozen chairs and there was the all-pervading smell of incense. It was an Orthodox Church in miniature.

In the few months he had been in the village, he did muster half a dozen regular members of his congregation, all ladies of means. Lonely ladies, I believed. Ladies with husbands out at work all day and absent for most of the night.

Severus remained with us for more than a year and not once did I receive any complaint about him or his church. I did make discreet enquiries into his claims and into his name and background, but found absolutely nothing. Other than searching his house, I realized I could learn nothing of the man – and I could not search his house unless he was arrested for a crime.

Then it became known that he had had a calling to visit America, there to establish yet another of his monasteries. Notices appeared on the parish noticeboard and in the local paper; there were papers pinned to the door of his church because he was attempting to raise funds to finance his visit to America on a missionary basis. And, of course, the rich ladies provided their support. They organized events in the village like raffles, jumble sales, whist drives and other gatherings with the sole aim of raising money for his charitable and religious work in the pagan USA.

And, sufficient funds having been raised, he conducted a thanksgiving service in his church, thanked everyone for their support and left Aidensfield.

The cottage remained empty for a long time, and the caravan with the onion on its roof began to look rather neglected.

No more ladies came to pray there, although some did receive postcards from America signed 'Severus' and saying it was a wonderful country for the free and that he had managed to establish several small churches in various neighbourhoods. But there was no address or contact number on any of the correspondence, and no hint about where precisely those churches had been established In time, Maddleskirk Abbey Trustees recovered their caravan, took the onion and leek off its roof then removed the icon and other adornments. It was needed to house a new cowman who worked on the abbey farm.

And that, I reckoned, was the end of Father Severus, except that two or three years later I was watching a colourful police thriller at a local Odeon. I forget the title now, but suddenly, in a daring sequence where a trapped man leapt from a high building which was on fire and threatening to collapse, I saw Father Severus. He was the man who was about to jump; his tall, powerful figure, his handsome face with its beard and thick hair were unmistakable and then I realized why he had gone to America. There he would find lots of pretty women with plenty of money but I don't think they would be the kind who'd be happy spending their spare time in a caravan with an onion on the roof. In Hollywood, there was a different religion and he had found it – but he looked very happy.

When the credits came up, I saw that the stuntman was called Igor Stepnyak. I wondered if the American police would try and establish who precisely he was.

But, as I had had no complaints from Hollywood, it was not my job.

If priests and vicars were prey to confidence tricksters, then so were the occupiers and owners of large country houses. One of their chief difficulties was the recruiting of reliable and trustworthy members of staff; even when landowners were being penalized relentlessly by the advance of socialism, they did manage to keep their homes and life style. They found new methods of keeping the homes which had been in the family for centuries, even if it meant opening them to the public.

Fortunately, many were still able to provide much-needed employment for local people, but it was a changing world which forced them to advertise for staff. Fewer and fewer recruits could be found in the surrounding villages and many young people would not tolerate the long hours, high demands and meagre wages which accompanied this kind of work. The outcome was that even though butlers, housemaids, laundrymaids, gardeners, estate workers and their kind were still in demand by the owners of mansions on my beat, such staff had to be recruited from afar, often from towns and cities, and often from a class of person lacking loyalty, honour and trustworthiness. Gone were the days when you could hire a maid or a manservant for life; no longer was it considered an honour to work for his Lordship. Rather, it was considered to be drudgery.

But the polish of a trained butler was still necessary and who better to fill the role of butler than a highly skilled confidence trickster?

Many of them did apply for such posts and many were appointed, only for his Lordship to discover later that items of the family silver or priceless bottles of wine from his cellar had vanished, often at the same time that the butler no longer responded to his bell.

Our circulars were rich with examples of this kind of treachery and theft and we did try to educate their Lordships into taking care over staff appointments. One simple method was to actually check any proffered references. Many prospective employers, in places ranging from factories to fancy houses, took written references on face value without checking that the signature was genuine or that the supposed signatory had, in fact, written such glowing prose about the chap applying for the post.

There is a theory, of course, that if a referee writes highly praiseworthy words about an employee, then it is done with a desire to part company with that employee. The ploy was often used in the police force. If an officer in one force was not very proficient, he usually had an unhappy time and felt that a transfer to a quieter area would be beneficial. When he applied for a post in the new force of his choice, his chief would write glowing praises about him, in the hope that someone would be daft enough to take him off his hands.

Sometimes, that ploy worked, but very soon discerning chief constables realized that high praise from another chief constable was often an indication that he was trying to offload some rubbish. It was akin to the prose of a second-hand car salesman or a less-than-honest antique dealer. You finished with something that looked good but which did not work. In those respects, second-hand policemen were often like second-hand cars.

In our attempts to thwart confidence tricksters, we tried to educate all potential employers to check references with great care and, until the Labour Government said it was wrong for us to check a person's criminal record in such cases, we could even make discreet enquiries on their behalf. After all, it was in the interests of the local constabulary and also the local community not to have a known and active criminal living in the village, even if he was employed at the big house at the end of the drive and even if he said he'd reformed.

But the socialist creed said otherwise – the socialists said we must give all villains a fair chance to continue their crimes. And so they did. With no check on their activities and precious little punishment to deter them, they continued to commit their crimes and to accumulate an increasing list of victims. But in the days preceding those doctrinaire edicts, we did check a person's criminal record if he or she was applying for certain posts and I do know that a lot of crime was thus prevented.

In spreading the message of caution when making vital appointments I did, I know, influence Lord Ashfordly on more than one occasion. Several checks of submitted references proved to be false and as a consequence, he did not make the appointments in question. Today, of course, the Theft Act of 1968, section 16, deals with dishonestly obtaining a pecuniary advantage by deception and this now makes it a crime to obtain a job with forged references or through the use of invalid or faked qualifications.

But even the most careful checks can fail to flush out a clever villain and so it was with a butler appointed by Lord Ashfordly.

He called himself Gilbert Chaldecott-Montefiore and upon applying for the post of butler with Lord Ashfordly, had produced glowing references from his last employer, the Earl of Labberford. He had worked for the earl at his London house, so he had claimed.

Lord Ashfordly, not knowing Labberford in person, had written to the impressive address on the high quality headed paper and had received a reply to the effect that Chaldecott-Montefiore was a splendid fellow worthy of anyone's hire. He had left Labberford's employment simply because Labberford, a widower of some years, was going into a private nursing home for an extended period and would not therefore require a butler in the foreseeable future. Lord Ashfordly had congratulated himself upon the acquisition of such an outstanding chap.

In fact, Lord Ashfordly was so pleased with his new butler that for once he did not ask me to discreetly check his credentials.

But in the weeks that followed, the demeanour of Gilbert Chaldecott-Montefiore led his Lordship to believe that the fellow was not everything that he claimed. His knowledge of fine wines was very limited, his treatment of the other servants was not in keeping with his position of butler, his attitude to Lord Ashfordly's guests was not of the kind one would attribute to a trained man . . . .

Lord Ashfordly, with the beginnings of suspicion deep in his heart, rang me one morning.

'Ah, Mr Rhea,' he always called me Mr Rhea, not just Rhea, 'I would like a word with you, on a private matter.'

'I'll be in your area this afternoon,' I said. 'I could call around three o'clock?'

'That will be perfect.' He sounded relieved.

Wondering what could be worrying him, I drove to Ashfordly Park, his magnificent country house, and rang the bell. It sounded deep within the mansion and a maid responded. When I announced that his Lordship was expecting me, I was asked to wait in the library, and was eventually shown into the study. A silver tray of tea and biscuits was waiting, and the maid poured a cup for each of us before handing around the biscuits. As she worked, Lord Ashfordly made small talk about the weather and increasing tourism in the market town which bore his name.

When she'd left us, he began, 'This is a delicate matter, Mr Rhea. I must insist on complete confidence and the utmost discretion on your part.'

'Of course,' I assured him. I liked Lord Ashfordly. A sturdy man in his early fifties with a good head of hair, he was a tireless worker for the townspeople, sitting on the parish council and the county council and protecting the town against unwelcome development. He had a known dislike of square concrete buildings and characterless shopping developments and, fortunately for Ashfordly town, was in a position to resist hurtful change. I had a lot of respect for him.

'Last month,' he said, 'I appointed a new butler, a man called Gilbert Chaldecott-Montefiore. Excellent references, good bearing, fine manner, good command of the English language, smart and tidy. Ideal in many ways. You've met him, have you?'

'No, I haven't,' I said, explaining that from time to time I did meet the butlers of such houses, but to date, had not had the pleasure of the company of Mr Gilbert Chaldecott-Montefiore.

'It is his day off today,' smiled Ashfordly. 'He has gone to Scarborough, there's an outing been arranged from the town; he's away all day, hence my call to you.'

'You are worried about him?' I anticipated. 'He hasn't been stealing from you, has he?'

'I fear that might follow,' and he told me about his worries which were chiefly based on his butler's lack of finesse and skill in his chosen profession. As his Lordship itemized the growing number of small errors, I realized they were the kind of fault I would never have recognized, nor indeed would any ordinary person. But to a blue-blooded member of the British aristocracy, those errors and lack of the social graces would be like loud warning bells. With reasonable cause for concern, Lord Ashfordly suspected that the fellow was a charlatan.

'So, Mr Rhea,' he said. 'I am asking if there is any way you can check his antecedents for me?'

I had no wish for a theft to be committed at Lord Ashfordly's house; worse still, it might become an unsolved crime if the villain was very clever. And no self-respecting constable wants an unsolved crime on his books. I was therefore keen to help.

'His name,' I proffered. 'Is it genuine? It sounds more like the name of an employer than an employee.'

'That's the name he uses, Mr Rhea, and it was on all his documents; medical card, National Insurance and so on.'

'Thanks.' I knew that it was not difficult to obtain forged documents of that kind. 'Have you any of the papers he supplied to you? References and so on? I need something to base my enquiries upon.'

'There's his personal file, in the safe. I'll get it.'

Unlocking his safe, he produced a file of papers and passed them across. I made notes of the names, addresses and other salient factors provided by Gilbert Chaldecott-Montefiore in applying for the post, and returned the file to him. I then asked for a physical description of the butler and was told he appeared to be between thirty-five and forty years of age, his documents showing him to be thirty-eight. He was 5' 11'' tall, well built without a beer drinker's belly, dark hair cut short and kept tidy with a regular application of hair-oil, no bald patch, good strong white teeth, grey eyes, clean shaven and he did not wear spectacles. He was always smartly dressed and when off duty favoured a dark blue blazer with the top pocket bearing a badge depicting a yacht, a white shirt, a striped tie and grey trousers. He was well spoken with no discernible accent, but did not own a car or any transport of his own. He had no known tattoos or other obvious identifying features.

'I'll check our records,' I assured him. 'We do have a pool of information about confidence tricksters who are operating up and down the country but if this name has not been used before, we might have trouble identifying him. His description could fit thousands of men. But I'll let you know what progress I make.'

I ran a check with our local criminal record office and with the national CRO in Scotland Yard, but the name of Gilbert Chaldecott-Montefiore was not listed as a suspicious character.

Likewise, I asked the Metropolitan Police in London to find out if the Earl of Labberford was resident at the address given by the butler. They said it would take a few days to produce an answer.

As I suspected, the butler's physical description was of little value, a surprising number of active con men having a similar appearance. Having done this, rather than show my uniform at the Park when the butler was working, I rang Lord Ashfordly with my lack of positive news.

'What I need, sir,' I told him, 'is a set of his fingerprints. If he has been convicted, they'll be on record. Can you get them for me, surreptitiously?'

'How on earth would I do that?' he chortled.

'I need to have something he has handled, something with a smooth surface like a wine-glass, a bottle of wine perhaps, or a piece of silver, an ashtray maybe, something that his prints will adhere to. And you would not have to touch it either . . . you will need to persuade him to handle the object and then leave it in your office, without anyone else touching it, for me to collect . . . you could ask him for an opinion about a new wine, perhaps? A glass would be better than a bottle, it has no paper label. Paper doesn't show prints very well.'

'Got you!' Lord Ashfordly sounded pleased. 'Leave it with me, I'll call you when I've done my Sherlock Holmes bit.'

It would be three days later when he called me.

'Mr Rhea,' he almost whispered into the telephone, 'I have a wine-glass which our friend has handled, no one else has touched it.'

'I'll be there right away,' I promised him.

Lord Ashfordly told me he'd asked the butler to test a new claret and the fellow had used the glass which now stood on a tray on a side table in the office. The butler had offered to clear away the glass after the tasting, but his Lordship had suggested he leave it for the maid. After all, that was her job. And then Lord Ashfordly had locked the tray and the glass in his safe. I took possession of both the tray and glass.

Taking infinite care with the samples, I placed them in a secure box and took them home from where I rang our Force Scenes of Crime department and asked if they would check the items for fingerprints. I told them the full story and completed the necessary forms. They said it would be no problem. Two days later, the SOCO van arrived, having been on another investigation in the vicinity, and a detective constable took away the exhibits.

The next day, I received a telephone call from Lord Ashfordly.

'He's gone,' he said. 'Chaldecott-Montefiore has left my employ, Mr Rhea. He's just vanished. Gone like a puff of wind.'

'Has he taken anything from the house?' was my first question. 'Anything of yours, I mean.'

'No, not a thing. He's just packed his bags and left, he's not even taken his personal papers.'

'He'll get some new ones in another name,' I said. 'He doesn't need the ones he's left behind. Did he give a reason?'

'Not to me, but I've asked the other staff if they know why he left. It seems he had words with the maid about the removal of that wine-glass, Mr Rhea, and she said she'd not moved it nor even seen it . . . I think he was suspicious of what I'd done, I think we flushed him out, Mr Rhea.'

'All that suggests he *was* a con man,' I laughed. 'But our own results aren't through yet. I'll let you know what turns up, sir. You'll be applying for a new butler now?'

'Well, actually, there is a chap in town, he had to leave his post as waiter in one of my hotels, not in the best of health, you know, but I think he can cope here, so I'm offering him the post. And I do know him of old, Mr Rhea.'

The Metropolitan Police did ring to say there was no record of anyone called the Earl of Labberford, and that the address was now occupied by tenants who were law-abiding and who had no idea who either Labberford or Chaldecott-Montefiore were. When the results of the fingerprint check came through, I learned they belonged to a confidence trickster whose real name was Charles Brown. He had a string of convictions in dozens of false names which included Crispin Carnegy, Nicholas Rochford, Auriel Blake-Edwards, Guy Furness-Brown, Dougal MacTavish-Rochford, Benedict Irvine, Peter Charles Monthiem-Muirhead, Derek Kelligan, Owen Walwyn-Jones and many more. His last conviction had resulted in two years' imprisonment for stealing silver from a country house where he had secured work as the butler.

I rang Lord Ashfordly to acquaint him with the character he'd welcomed to his home, and also to say that it looked as though the Earl of Labberford was also a fictional character. He thanked me, saying he was pleased that our joint actions had warned off the villain before he'd had the chance to steal anything.

Lord Ashfordly did say he'd done some of his own detective work too, by using his London contacts, and he had also discovered that the supposed Earl of Labberford did not exist. The address was genuine, it had been rented for a few months by a man called Jean-Paul Vericompte who had vanished. His appearance was remarkably similar to that of Gilbert Chaldecott-Montefiore. Lord Ashfordly was able to tell me more than Scotland Yard had bothered to unearth.

'The cunning of the fellow!' Lord Ashfordly had apparently enjoyed his piece of detective work and I felt he would relate the tale at many a dinner party. 'Damned clever really, it's a shame he was such a villain. If he'd used his brains properly, he might have been a success in life. Charming fellow, Mr Rhea, damned good in many ways. Sorry to burden you with my problems.'

'Not at all,' I said. 'That's why I'm here, to prevent crime.'

'I wonder where he's gone?' asked Lord Ashfordly.

Nine months later, our circulars told the story of the theft of a substantial amount of silver-plate from a mansion at Arridgeford in the Yorkshire Dales. The butler, who'd vanished, was the chief suspect; he had given the name of Ogden Garnon-Evans but his description was remarkably similar to that of Gilbert Chaldecott-Montefiore.

I rang the village constable at Arridgeford with an account of my own experience at Ashfordly and said we had a set of fingerprints if they were of any value.

Then I rang Lord Ashfordly to pass on that piece of news – it would add to the stories he would relate to his guests.

3   Do You Really Have To Go?

I pray thee leave.

Michael Drayton (1563–1631)

Most of us have had the experience of guests who have out-stayed their welcome, but by any known standards, the staying power of Henry Hubert Houghton was exceptional.

Shortly after my arrival at Aidensfield, I heard his name mentioned in hushed tones and was advised not to show the hand of friendship towards him. Being fairly new to the district, I understood this to indicate that Henry was a rogue of some kind, or an undesirable fellow, the likes of which young constables should not befriend, but when I first saw him, he seemed a perfectly reasonable gentleman. Middle-aged, well spoken, smartly dressed and of fairly affluent means, he looked like any normal middle-class man albeit with perhaps just a hint of being rather vague. A fine head of greying hair with a hint of lingering ginger, a profuse moustache, a penchant for smoking a pipe full of pungent tobacco and a wardrobe full of expensive, tweedy clothes placed him firmly within the county set, and certainly not within the realms of local villains. I don't think he followed a profession but he did seem to have a fairly comfortable life style; he was a bachelor who lived in a large house and ran a vintage Rolls Royce.

Most certainly, there was no reason to suspect that he was a sexual deviant, mentally sick or a villain of any kind, so why should I keep him at a distance? I was enlightened somewhat further when another villager warned me never to invite Henry Hubert Houghton for dinner or even for a cup of coffee.

'I've already had a veiled warning about him, but he seems a decent enough chap,' I said. 'He's not a rogue so I'm at a loss to know why I should keep clear of him.'

'Oh, he's decent enough, and honest,' said my informant. 'But there's one major problem with him – if he gets into your house, he'll never leave. He'll be there all night, mark my words. And I mean all night, not just an extra hour or two. That's the problem with Henry, he just won't go home.'

When I first heard this, I thought it was an indication that Henry perhaps stayed a fraction longer than was mannerly, something that lots of people did from time to time, but I was to learn that this was an understatement. If Henry got into anyone's house, he stayed – and stayed – and stayed.

My first direct experience of this phenomenon came from Dr Alex Ferrenby. I espied the bearded doctor ambling down the village street around ten o'clock one morning; he looked as if he'd been up all night for his hair was awry and there were large black rings around his eyes.

'You look a bit rough, doctor,' I smiled at him.

'Rough?' he coughed. 'I look a bit rough, I feel a bit rough and I am a bit rough. More than a bit rough, Nick, old son. I'm shattered, mentally, physically and emotionally.'

'Anything I can do?'

'Nope, not a thing. I've got my football pools to get off today – got to get my priorities right – so I'm off to the post office for a postal order and then, God willing, I'll crash out on the surgery lounger for a few hours.'

'A late night call out, was it?'

'Nothing of the sort,' grunted the old doctor. 'I wish it had been. No, it was that confounded fellow Houghton. I should never have invited him, I know him well enough to avoid having him, but, well, it was his birthday and I felt sorry for him. So he came for a meal last night and just would not go. I mean, I tried, I said it was bedtime, I even put my pyjamas on and the milk bottles out, but he just stayed and stayed . . . I went to bed and left him – he was still there this morning, sitting on my settee with a glass of whisky in his hands. I've left him again just now, perhaps he's still there!'

'I've heard about his staying power,' I chuckled. 'I thought it was exaggerated local folk lore or common talk.'

'Talk? It's not mere talk, old son, it's genuine. He just won't go. Don't you ever let him come to you for dinner,

Nick; he'll stay all night. I mean it. That's good advice from a sincere friend.'

Over a period of months, I began to hear other like tales of Henry Hubert Houghton and warned Mary about him, not that we would have any reason to invite him as a guest. But it did make sense to be prepared for the worst. I began to wonder how I would persuade him to leave should we ever be faced with the problem. Short of physically carrying him from the premises there seemed no polite way of persuading him to leave.

I was to learn that Dr Ferrenby had literally propelled him from the house. Others had done likewise – and Henry Hubert was never offended by these drastic measures. Indeed, such treatment became normal for those who had to deal with him and I began to suspect that he had come to terms with the fact that all his departures would be forced upon him. I think he had reached the stage where he would never leave unless someone pushed him out of the house. One clever lady had offered to take him shopping in York upon finding him still sitting in her lounge when she came down for breakfast and he'd gone shopping with her, but once in York, she'd managed to lose him among a crowd of American visitors. Somehow or other, he'd found his own way home. It seems that the ploys for evacuating Henry Hubert were many and varied, and I did realize that his vagueness and lack of appreciation of events going on around him meant he was never upset by this treatment. Armed with this knowledge, I felt sure I could cope should I be faced with such a problem.

It was inevitable in a small village like Aidensfield that the challenge would eventually arise – and so it did. I was about to leave home at 8.30 one morning for a patrol of Aidensfield and district in my police van, when the telephone rang. I answered it to find a distraught lady at the other end. It was Mrs Riley who lived in a fine house overlooking the green at Slemmington.

'Mr Rhea,' she breathed. 'Thank God I caught you . . . Henry Hubert is here, he's been here all night just sitting in my lounge and I must go out, I've an appointment, but he won't leave . . . can you help me?'

I hesitated. Domestic matters of this kind were hardly within the scope of a police officer's duty, but in a rural community, the constable always tries to help where possible. This seemed a good means of establishing good relations with the public while helping a lady in dire distress.

'I'll be there in twenty minutes,' I promised her.

Mrs Riley, a handsome woman in her late thirties, was waiting at the front door, wringing her hands and almost on the point of tears. 'Oh I do hope I'm not being a nuisance, but he just won't go . . . my husband asked him to join us for dinner last night, Mr Rhea, God knows why. When it got to midnight we dropped hints but he just sat and sat, and so, in the end, in sheer desperation, we went to bed and left him on the sofa. He was still sitting there this morning, I don't think he'd been to sleep and I don't think he even noticed we'd gone to bed.'

'He's always like this,' and I explained what I'd learned about the fellow. 'I'll take him home.'

'I would be so grateful,' she sighed. 'I really would.'

'Come along, Henry.' I gently eased him to his feet by taking his arm. 'Time to go home.'

'Oh, really? That's awfully kind of you, Mr Rhea,' and he thanked Mrs Riley for a splendid meal and warm hospitality. He seemed to think that whatever was happening to him was quite normal and as he had no transport of his own, having come by taxi, I settled him in the passenger seat of my police van. He sat there very quietly, rather like a huge warm teddy bear, but when I was driving away from Slemmington, the radio burbled into life with my call sign. I responded, hoping this wasn't a call-out to an emergency for I didn't want to be lumbered with Henry Hubert if I had to cope with a traffic accident or anything else of a serious nature.

'Location please,' requested the radio set and I recognized the distinctive voice of Sergeant Blaketon broadcasting from Ashfordly police station.

'Slemmington, heading towards Brantsford and Ashfordly,' I responded.

'Received. Please attend High Row House, Thackerston, home of a Miss Morris. Report of intruders. Over.'

Thackerston was some distance from my present location so I asked, 'Understood. ETA – twenty minutes. Is there another mobile in the vicinity who can attend more speedily?'

'Negative,' came Blaketon's blunt response. 'This is not considered urgent, the intruder might be a cat in the loft. The lady has heard noises up there. You're on duty, Rhea, you're the nearest, you will attend. Over.'

'Ten four,' I responded.

If I drove Henry Hubert home first, it would add a further quarter of an hour on to the journey to Thackerston even if I could get him out of the van immediately; I wondered why Sergeant Blaketon couldn't have driven to Thackerston to check out the intruder report; he was much closer than I and could be on the scene before I reached the halfway stage. As I pondered the reasons for his lethargy, I did wonder if he was perhaps afraid of searching lofts for things that made mysterious noises . . . but of course, I would never suggest that! As I drove along, I felt it would be a risk taking Henry Hubert with me. If he settled himself into High Row House over a cup of Miss Morris's coffee, he'd be there all day and he might even stay all night too. In view of the lack of urgency and the suggestion that there was no rampaging housebreaker, I decided to offload Henry *en route*, and what better place than Ashfordly police station? As my journey took me right past the front door, it would, I hoped, be a simple matter to drop off Henry and he would have a bit of companionship too because Sergeant Blaketon was clearly *in situ*, keeping out of the way of nerve-racking tasks. I felt Henry Hubert would be a good companion for Sergeant Blaketon!

Minutes later, I drove into the yard of Ashfordly police station, helped Henry Hubert out of the cramped little van and escorted him into the front passage of our highly polished police station.

'Who's this, Rhea?' Sergeant Blaketon looked up from his typewriter as I bustled Henry inside. The expression on Blaketon's face indicated that he thought I'd arrested a housebreaker. I had to disillusion him.

'This is Mr Houghton, Sergeant, he was stranded at Slemmington and I was taking him home when I got your call. He lives in Aidensfield. But I thought, in view of the urgency of my call-out, I could drop him here, he can catch a bus home from the market-place. There's a timetable on our noticeboard, that's why I brought him, to have a look at it. . . .'

'Rhea, you are not supposed to give members of the public lifts in official vehicles except in an emergency duty situation.

We are not a taxi service . . . .'

As he launched into the official ruling about the use and misuse of official vehicles, I rushed out, jumped into the van and roared away towards Thackerston. I chuckled to myself – I thought my disposal of Henry Hubert had been very neatly done and I congratulated myself.

When I arrived at Miss Morris's pretty cottage, she told me how she'd heard strange noises in the loft; they were still there. I listened. It was weird, a sort of scratching sound accompanied by loud rustling movements in the roof void.

I could understand why a maiden lady in her seventies should be worried. I made a search of the house downstairs and could find no sign of a forcible entry and she said she'd not let anyone in. The cottage was detached and so it was impossible for anyone to creep into the loft from adjoining premises; the loft door was in position above the landing and so I was sure there was no one lurking up there. However, I decided to climb in to investigate.

I discovered that the noises came from a pair of starlings. They had entered the loft through a hole beneath the tiles and were busy constructing their nest. The sound of their claws and the rustling of their movements among the rubble and the loft insulation had been amplified – this kind of problem was a regular event for country folk. Upon my arrival, the birds fled through the hole and flew off, so I blocked it with some heavy pieces of rubble I found lying about the loft. I didn't think they'd be able to return.

She was very relieved when I explained and offered me coffee. Having dealt with this intruder, I relaxed over the warm drink, then radioed Ashfordly police station to make a situation report. Sergeant Blaketon answered.

'Ten four,' he acknowledged, and then added, 'Rhea, that man you brought is still here, he will not leave to catch his bus . . . I have asked him to go, I even gave him a coffee at my own expense, but he's just sitting on the bench in our entrance hall . . . you'd better come and take him away.'

'I'm not supposed to use my official vehicle for carrying members of the public,' I reminded him. 'Besides, Sergeant, I have an appointment at The Aidensfield Arms in quarter of an hour, I'm meeting the chairman of the parish council to discuss an occasional licence for a parish event . . . .'

'But, Rhea, this fellow will not leave the police station, I can't get him out . . . .'

'I'm sure a man of your vast experience will cope with him, Sergeant,' I said. 'Over and out.'

Some unfortunate people will refuse to leave premises for perfectly sound reasons and such a person was Victor Pyman. For the whole of his working life, he had been employed upon Lord Ashfordly's estate. He had no particular trade but if anyone asked what he did for a living, he would say he was an estate worker. This included a wide range of skills, from felling and dressing timber to erecting and maintaining fences, hedging, building rough roads, repairing stonework and roofs, ditching, cutting grass, tractor driving and even repairing heavy machinery. Victor, like his father had been, was a very versatile man and an undoubted asset to his employer.

Indeed, so valued was Victor that the estate manager had agreed to keep him in employment even though he had passed the retiring age of sixty-five. But as he approached seventy, the estate manager, a Mr Taylor, felt it was time for Victor to retire. Victor had not wanted to finish but had reluctantly agreed.

Lately, he had begun to feel his age, a fact gently pointed out to him by Mr Taylor who had realized that Victor was slowing down and tiring easily. Besides, as Mr Taylor had pointed out, Victor had enough interests to keep him busy at home. During his life, he had assembled a large flock of hens which he kept at his cottage, he had pigeons in a loft, a family of ferrets, several Golden Retrievers, an unknown number of cats and even a tame roe deer. In retirement, he could spend more time with his beloved animals and so, at last, he warmed to the idea of having more free time.

During his life, he had been totally content in his work, his father having been employed in a similar capacity for the old Lord Ashfordly. Victor now lived in the house previously occupied by his father. That house was owned by the estate but it had been occupied by the Pymans for many years. Victor had been born there and had lived there as a child; indeed, he had lived there all his life, sharing the house with his parents until their deaths. He had married late, but had produced no children and his wife had died some five years before I came into contact with him. Now, therefore, Victor was the sole occupant but, having no heirs, the family's long occupancy of that quiet woodland cottage would come to an end when Victor departed.

I was never sure how Mr Taylor intended to deal with Victor's cottage so far as his retirement was concerned because, sadly, Mr Taylor died suddenly from a heart attack.

We shall never know what his intentions were because it was the long-standing practice of the estate that, unless there were siblings who continued to work for the estate, the occupants of estate-owned houses would have to vacate the premises upon their retirement. Alternative accommodation would be found for them and their family. If there were no available estate cottages, then a council house would be arranged.

The way for a family to retain an estate-owned house was to persuade one of their offspring to work for Lord Ashfordly and in the past, lots of them had done this. They had thus remained in their home, with their parents living with them in retirement. Through this system, an estate cottage was occupied by the same family for many generations and many had died in the house in which they had been born. But in the 1960s, there was a changing attitude towards working for the aristocracy and there was no commitment to the continuity of family service. Young people were moving away and besides, few desired to be employed in what they regarded as humble work. When their parents retired, therefore, there was no one to take over the family home on the estate. Other workers moved in, often being recruited from afar, and few had the commitment of those past workers. Some cottages, located in Ashfordly town, were sold and so the overall atmosphere on the estate had changed dramatically within a few years.

For Victor, therefore, having followed in his father's footsteps, there had been no trouble finding a house – he had simply continued to live in the cottage where he had spent his happy childhood, and now, approaching the age of seventy, he hoped he would be allowed to die in peace in the same old house. But if Mr Taylor had intended to allow Victor to remain, he had never told anyone; he had died before making those intentions known either to Victor or to the estate management.

A new estate manager was appointed at rather short notice

and he arrived at this critical stage of Victor's life. Official wheels grind very slowly but very surely and quite suddenly, Victor found himself served with an order to quit Woodland Cottage. And if he went, it would mean that all his beloved livestock would also have to go. And you couldn't keep pigeons, hens, dogs, cats, ferrets and a pet deer in the garden of a town house or on a council estate.

It was Victor's misfortune that, at this critical moment of his life, there had been a change of estate manager. The newcomer was from Hertfordshire, a Mr Simon Furnace, and from the day of his appointment, things seemed to go wrong for Victor. There can be no excuses for sloppy work and bad personnel management, but there can be reasons. Victor was an unwitting key character in the sad drama which followed.

During the change-over from one regime to the other, there had been a lamentable breakdown in internal communications.

That was the reason that poor Victor found himself with a notice to quit Woodland Cottage. In fact, this was a perfectly normal procedure because the council would not rehouse people unless they'd been given an order to quit their tied houses. What normally happened was that people in Victor's position were told they would receive a formal notice to quit but not to regard it as anything personal; it was all part of the system and it was done so that they could then inform the council of that fact, and the council would have to rehouse them. If such tenants voluntarily left their tied houses, the council would not rehouse them. Thus these notices were important to the tenants, but due to an administrative clanger, no one had told Victor of the real purpose behind his notice. Mr Furnace probably thought Victor had been told by Mr Taylor, whereas he had not; there was no doubt Victor was under the impression he could stay in Woodland Cottage for the rest of his life.

The shock of receiving the notice to quit was almost fatal, but once he'd gathered himself together, he thought the estate was rejecting him after all those years of work. It is an under-statement to say he was extremely upset. In his loneliness, his sorrow turned to deep anger, and his deep anger turned into determination. He became determined that no one would force him, or his animals, to leave Woodland Cottage.

It is a fact in many such cases, that if there is a gross error at the outset, then that error is compounded during subsequent developments.

In his abject misery, poor old Victor did not seek help from anyone; from that initial anger and misery, his mood turned to one of dogged determination as he began to take measures to barricade his home against all-comers. The new management, on the other hand, became increasingly agitated at the old man's determination to stay put and could not understand his attitude. As time went on, Victor passed the age of seventy and thus ceased to be employed by the estate, but he stubbornly refused to leave the cottage, and so the estate's notice to quit was eventually reinforced by a court order. A copy was served on Victor. Even at that stage, the management thought Victor would have taken steps to secure for himself a council house, or at least would have warned the council of his impending homelessness, but that had not happened. Victor had no intention of living in a council house. He was sitting tight in the only home he had known as the official wheels were put inexorably in motion. Victor was about to be evicted.

The lack of communication, which grew worse instead of better, convinced Mr Furnace that Victor was a troublemaker, and Victor regarded Furnace as an evil man who now represented the true nature of Lord Ashfordly. Furnace became determined to have the old man out of Woodland Cottage with the minimum of fuss because, he claimed, it was needed for a new estate worker, while Victor was determined to stay with his menagerie. It seemed that an unhappy confrontation of some kind was inevitable.

At that time, one of the worst duties that could befall a police constable was to be ordered to attend an eviction. When a tenant ignored the court order to quit the premises, the next stage was for the bailiffs to move in.

Quite literally, the bailiffs' task was to remove all the furniture and belongings of the tenant, then remove the tenant and secure the premises against the evicted person and/or the family. It was a very distasteful duty; it was even more

distasteful for the police officer who had to attend. Every
police officer hated being associated with this sort of thing, for
their duty was not to evict the family – their duty was to
prevent a breach of the peace. It was inevitable, however, that
the victims of the court order regarded the police as officers
who were helping to enforce the court order. This was not so –
enforcement of such court orders was never a police matter
but as we stood by to prevent fights and attacks on all parties,
it was inevitable that we got the blame.

There was, however, a little-known Act of Parliament called
the Small Tenements Recovery Act of 1838, still in force in the
1960s, by which a warrant could order a police officer to effect
an entry, by force if necessary, to eject the tenant and remove
his furnishings so that the owner could recover possession of
rented accommodation. I thanked God that I had never known
that statue ever be used in my part of Yorkshire and that I had
never had to enforce such an order. And I hoped I never
would be put in that terrible position.

It was with some trepidation, therefore, that I found myself
instructed to present myself at Woodland Cottage, there to
prevent a breach of the peace while bailiffs evicted the tenant,
a Mr Victor Pyman. This was the first intimation I'd had of
any trouble with Victor – and I thanked God that I was not
being ordered to carry out the eviction.

I decided to visit Mr Furnace, the new estate manager, to
find out precisely what had prompted the issue of legal process
in this case. As he called me into his office with its stuffed
birds, display of antlers and beautifully polished oak
panelling, the first thing that impressed me was his utter
pomposity and total lack of interest in people. What on earth
had prompted Lord Ashfordly to appoint him was beyond me.
He was one of those rare people who immediately persuade
others to dislike them.

'The facts are clear, Constable.' A tall, fair-haired man with a
narrow, cruel face, he stood with his back to the fireplace of his
office with his heels on the fender, and he did not offer me a seat
or a coffee. 'The stupid oaf will not leave the house, the house
belongs to the estate, and the estate is seeking repossession.
Pyman has been there five years longer than normal, he's had all

the time in the world to secure another home. It's time for him to go, that's all there is to it. It's my job to house my current workers and I need that cottage for a new man. Pyman has had the usual notice to quit, which he has ignored.'

'Perhaps he needs help,' I ventured. 'He is an old man.'

'That is not my function, Mr Rhea. The situation is that Pyman is ignoring the court order to vacate the house. Your job, as I understand it, is to stop Pyman doing anything stupid, like shooting at us or attacking the bailiffs. I fail to see why you need to come and discuss it with me.'

I could see Furnace's secretary looking at me through the adjoining door as Furnace pontificated from his fireside perch, and I knew by her face that she, and, I suspected, the other office staff, were far from happy with this idiot in charge. As he bore on about maintaining the efficiency of the estate, I found myself incredulous at what I was hearing. I knew Victor was not the troublemaker that this fellow was implying and I realized the poor old fellow could never expect a sympathetic hearing from this obnoxious character. But duty was duty. As a policeman, I was supposed to do my duty without fear or favour but I must admit that my sympathies were with Victor.

Even if it might be said I was exceeding my duties, I decided to have a word with Victor. Having listened to Furnace I was uncertain about my reception from poor old Victor, but went to see him none the less. I parked on a grassy area beneath some sycamores within sight of Woodland Cottage and walked towards the building. Hens were pecking about the place and at my approach, two of Victor's retrievers barked and raced towards the white-painted fence which surrounded the house.

I noticed Victor's pale face at one of the downstairs windows and waved towards him.

'Victor, it's me, PC Rhea,' I shouted. 'Can I have a word?'

The window opened and Victor shouted, 'What do you want?'

'A word with you,' I called back. 'A quiet word.'

'There's nowt to say, Mr Rhea. If you've come to chuck me out, I'm not going and that's that.'

'I haven't come to chuck you out, Victor. I've come for a chat.'

'You think I believe that? All them papers I've got, threatening me with bailiffs . . . .'

'Victor, those papers are nothing to do with me or my colleagues.' I stood my ground. 'I just want a chat.'

He hesitated; he was from a generation who could trust the police and I did know he'd been friendly towards the Ashfordly officers in the past. Victor was a true countryman, as honest as a person could be.

'Hang on,' he said, closing the window. Minutes later the front door opened and he peered out, as if checking to see if I had any colleagues concealed among the trees, but when he was satisfied I was alone, he bade me enter. We went into his kitchen where a kettle was singing on an old-fashioned hob over the fire. Without a word, he made a pot of tea, produced some scones from a tin and pointed to a chair at the polished pine table.

I told him I had just come from Furnace's office and explained what had transpired, then asked for his version of events. He told me, his old eyes brimming with tears as he related his family's long occupancy of Woodland Cottage, concluding by saying, 'And to think it's all come to this, chucking me out with nowhere to go . . . it's disgraceful, I never thought his Lordship would stoop to such a thing, the old Lord would never have, he was good to his staff . . . .'

'Hang on, Victor,' I said. 'Has Lord Ashfordly spoken to you about this?'

'Spoken? No, how can he? He's in Switzerland, skiing, been there weeks . . . nobody knows where he is, he's touring, moving from hotel to hotel. He's due back on Wednesday but it'll be no good talking to him, not now, not when his office has done this.'

'Those papers, Victor, you've got them handy?'

'Aye, in my bureau,' and he produced a sheaf of them which he spread on the table. I fished through them, finding the notice to quit which the estate had issued, pinned to the back of which was another letter. This was a note explaining how, upon receipt of the notice to quit, the recipient should make application to the council to be rehoused; the note also explained that the purpose of the notice to quit was indeed to persuade the council to allocate a council house and it advised the recipient to take the notice to the council offices. Then I saw that the notice was dated almost ten months ago.

So poor old Victor *had* been notified of the procedures. I suspected he had not understood the purpose of the letters, which were couched in legal jargon. Or, of course, he had never even read the letter. In the shock of reading the notice, he might not have turned it over to study the small print attached to it. And, I was conscious of the fact that the deceased Mr Taylor might have promised he could remain in the cottage. But notwithstanding all those possibilities, it would have been good personnel management for someone to have come out and explained things to him in simple terms.

When I began to explain the contents, it was clear that he had not read all the correspondence, he had not discussed it with anyone nor had anyone come to enlighten him. I asked whether Taylor had made any promises about the house and he said, 'Well, he did say he'd keep me on, Mr Rhea, working. That meant I could stay here . . . .'

'But you know that when a person retires, the estate needs the house for someone else . . . .'

'Aye, well, but we've been here years, Mr Rhea, our family has used this old house for longer than I can remember and I thought I could stay.'

What precisely had been said to Victor was uncertain, but there was no doubt that the whole affair was, in simple terms, a cock-up. That he was being badly treated was not in doubt, at least not in my mind, and I did not know whether I could halt the relentless machinery of the British legal system.

The bailiffs were due on Thursday; it was Monday now.

When I explained it all to Victor, saying how other workers in his position had been found nice accommodation, he assumed his stubborn attitude.

'That's mebbe so, Mr Rhea, but I don't want a council house. I want to stay here, with my animals. That's all. It's not a lot to ask and I've not long for this world, not at my age.'

'So you're staying put?'

'Aye, I am. If they carry me out of here, Mr Rhea, they'll carry me to my grave.'

'Mr Furnace said they need the house for another worker,' I

said. 'You can't hold up the work of the estate.'

'There's no other worker coming here, it's just an excuse, Mr Rhea. They're going to turn this into a holiday cottage, they don't want more staff, they're cutting back on workers now. When I finish, they'll not replace me, Lord Ashfordly told me that himself, months ago.'

'Is that right about the cottage?' I asked. 'It's going to be used by holidaymakers?'

'It's as right as I'm standing here, Mr Rhea. My home, I was born here, and it'll be used by folks who don't know me and who don't care a jot . . . .'

This news did make me angry; it was not the fact that it was to become a holiday home but the fact that the estate had misled the authorities about the future use of the house.

I was also annoyed that an old man had been made to go through such agony and turmoil. At that moment, I decided that something should be done. But what?

'Leave it with me, Victor,' I said, hoping that I sounded confident I could help him. 'I'll see what I can do – but if I can't stop things, I might be back on Thursday,' and I explained why I might be back and that it wouldn't be a pleasant visit for either him or me. If I couldn't halt the inexorable wheels of the British legal process, he might not regard me in such a trusting manner.

As I left the cottage, I had no idea how I should tackle this problem; in truth, it was nothing to do with me and in that respect, Mr Furnace was correct. Even so, I could stick my neck out in a vain attempt to get the estate to reconsider their decision; I could alert Lord Ashfordly to the situation, but he was away until just before zero hour; I could speak again with Simon Furnace to ask him to rethink the situation and seek the court's permission to withdraw their warrant or I could have a word with the court authorities themselves about the legal aspect of supplying false information in order to obtain a warrant. That could, in some circumstances, be regarded as perjury, although I did know that the estate did have the right to evict Victor in any case. Whether the future use of the cottage as a holiday home was material to the issue in question was a matter for debate.

I could examine the Perjury Act of 1911 to research those crimes where perjury could be committed when making false declarations, not on oath, and not in a court of law. That looked like using a sledgehammer to crack the proverbial nut.

Brooding over Victor's plight, I drove home and was in a somewhat angry and subdued mood as I finished my shift. Mary had tea ready so I went upstairs to change, then came down for a few minutes with the children before eating.

'You're very quiet,' said Mary over the meal. 'Is something wrong?'

I told her about Victor's plight and she sympathized with him, but did remind me that it was not my duty to interfere in cases of that kind. If the estate had seen fit to issue legal process, then that was their business, not mine. That evening, I relaxed with the children and helped Mary get them ready for bed, then said, 'I think I'll pop to the pub for a drink. I feel like a pick-me-up.'

'You need cheering up!' she said. 'But don't take Victor's case to heart, it's nothing to do with you.'

'He needs help. Anyway, how about you?' I asked. 'Would you like to come? Mrs Quarry would come and baby-sit at short notice, I'm sure.'

'No, you go, I'm finishing a dress for Elizabeth.' Mary made a lot of clothes for our children and she was an expert with a needle and sewing-machine.

And so, shortly after nine o'clock, I walked down to The Brewer's Arms to enjoy a couple of pints of best bitter. I enjoyed these relaxed times with the local people for the pub was the centre of information for Aidensfield and district. And as I sipped my beer, I noticed Edmund Fowler enter the pub.

He was a freelance journalist whom I often came across in the magistrates' court and when he saw me, he asked if I wanted a drink. I accepted a pint, making a vow to buy him one in return.

As we chatted, with him probing for stories and me trying to avoid revealing professional secrets, I realized that Victor's plight would make a cracking tale for the press.

'Pint, Eddie?' I asked when he'd drained his glass.

'Thanks.'

I took him to a quiet corner and asked if he was interested in a good story. Naturally, he said he was. I told him about an old man who was being evicted from his family home so that it could be turned into a holiday cottage, and that the owners had wrongly claimed the house was required for another worker. Eddie Fowler recognized the potential of this tale, saying it was a story for the national papers, and so I gave him details. I did add that Lord Ashfordly had no idea of recent developments. He said he'd love to do the story and promised not to divulge my name as the source.

On the Wednesday morning, the sorry tale of Victor Pyman was front page news in the *Northern Echo*, the *Yorkshire Post* and several national dailies. There were pictures of Victor with his animals, with photographs of his mother and father, and a quote from Mr Furnace saying that a mistake appeared to have been made.

When I reported to Ashfordly police station on Thursday morning to rendezvous with the bailiffs, I was told that the warrant had been withdrawn. Victor would be allowed to remain in the cottage for the rest of his days.

I was to learn that, in order to make him qualify for the tenancy in accordance with the estate's rules, he had been offered a part-time post. Victor thus became an estate worker yet again – men like him never retire anyway.

When Lord Ashfordly heard about the rumpus upon his return, he speedily arranged a meeting which was designed to improve relations between his office workers and the rest of his staff. I think it worked, because the next time I went into the estate office in the course of my duty, I was offered a cup of coffee by the new estate manager.

Another case of reluctant departure was very different because it featured a hearse.

A man called Angus Warriner, who lived in a small house tucked behind the main street of Aidensfield, had discovered the rotting hearse years ago.

From time to time when I was passing on a Saturday afternoon, I would pop in to have a look at it because Angus was 'doing it up'. In fact, he'd been doing it up for years.

Week by week, however, there would be a small degree of progress, perhaps a corner of metal had been meticulously shaped to replace a missing corner, a decorative piece of ironwork on the exterior had been crafted or he had completed a unit for the interior, a brass rail perhaps or a discreetly fitted light. The hearse was in a multitude of pieces spread about his garage and I wondered if it would ever be put together in one piece; Angus seemed to have no plan, apparently doing odd jobs when he felt like it and not working to an identifiable system. But he was highly confident that he would achieve his objective, which was to put the hearse back on the road in its original black and shining glory complete with brass rails, wood-lined rear interior, subdued lighting and luxurious leather upholstery.

The story was as follows. About ten years before my arrival at Aidensfield, Angus had discovered the 1932 Austin hearse in an orchard at Lairsbeck. Complete but neglected, it was being used as a hen-house. Although it had been smothered in hen dirt and straw, the fabric had been fairly sound, if somewhat rusty in places, and Angus had persuaded the owner, a smallholder, to part with it for a modest but welcome sum.

Over the following years, Angus had spent hours restoring the old vehicle. Not being a mechanic, he had bought books, discovered photographs of similar models, talked to hearse users of the past and had steeped himself in the history of this model. He had scoured scrapyards and old village garages in his quest for genuine spares, he had escorted coffins to the graveyard to see how the vehicle operated and in truth he had become a veritable expert on this type of hearse.

Then, quite suddenly, the vehicle began to look like a hearse once again. From the heap of spare parts which had gathered around the shell over the years, a Phoenix-like hearse had reappeared.

'What do you think o' that then, Mr Rhea?' he said to me one Saturday morning.

'Wonderful,' I said looking around. 'You've really worked a miracle, Angus.'

'She's not quite finished yet, mind. There's bits o' wiring to connect up, lighting to fettle, engine to get in tune and then she'll need a complete respray and polish, but we're getting there. She'll be out on the road soon, that's when I get her tracking right . . . .'

There was always something else for Angus to do on the vehicle. Each time I called, Angus had not quite finished, but there could be no doubt that, instead of a pile of scrap pieces and an old shell where hens once clucked and mucked, there was now a gleaming hearse in all its former glory.

Now, when I called, it was standing there in his garage and then, one day in June when I popped in, I noticed that the entire garage floor was clean and empty. Everything had been swept up, the garage was tidy and in the centre, shining in the light which filtered through the windows, was the most beautiful vehicle I had ever seen. Shining black with highly polished chromium on its wheels, bumpers, windows and door handles, the interior of the rear portion was of some highly polished wood with glistening brass fittings.

'Listen to this engine, Mr Rhea.' He opened the door and the scent of polish emerged. He pressed the starter and the engine struck up; it purred like a sewing-machine.

'Wonderful,' I breathed. 'That's wonderful Angus, you must be a very proud man.'

'I am, Mr Rhea, I am,' he sighed. I wondered how he was going to fill in his spare time now that the hearse was finished, but said to him, 'Well, Angus, you'll be wanting to get it taxed and insured, eh? To take it out for a drive?'

'Nay, Mr Rhea, I'll not do that. She's far too good to take on t'road, I'd be frightened of rust and getting it damaged . . . she'll stay here, safe and sound. I can polish her from time to time, you see . . . .'

And so the hearse never saw the light of day. As the months went by, I still popped in, but the hearse was now gathering dust and when Angus took up breeding cats, some of them nested in the back of the lovely vehicle.

Many years afterwards, long after I had left Aidensfield, I saw a report that Angus had died. I never went back into that garage, but I wondered if the old hearse was still there, full of cats and waiting for someone to come and do it up.

4 She Who Wears the Trousers

Lord of yourself, uncumber'd with a wife.
John Dryden (1631–1700)

Society, especially the male section of it, has always had to tolerate bossy, nagging and bad-tempered women. This trend continues in spite of a curious range of punishments designed to stay the whiplash of their cruel and muscular tongues.

One such implement was the ducking-stool; this was a type of seesaw or similar device, one end of which extended over a pond or river. The scold was seated upon the end which protruded over the water while the operators controlled the other end. At the appropriate time, the unfortunate woman was lowered into the water, perhaps several times, in an attempt to stop her tongue, but there are reports of women emerging with their tongues still going at full throttle.

A similar device was known as the cucking-stool but this was not used over water; an example of its role occurred at Leicester in 1467. It was known as 'a seat of infamy where strumpets and common scolds with bare feet and head were condemned to abide the derision of those who passed by'. In Leicester's case, it was operated by the mayor and the offending women were placed on the cucking-stool before their own doors, and then carried to the four gates of the town.

There are reports of large spheres of bare female flesh other than heads and feet being on display, because some cucking-stools sported a large hole in the seat.

One vicious punishment for scolds was the brank, sometimes known as the scold's bridle or gossip's bridle. The people of Macclesfield referred to their scold's bridle as 'a brydle for a curste queane'. The brank was a metal frame, rather like a heavy cage, which was placed over the woman's head and locked in position. At the point where her mouth faced the framework, there was a protruding piece of metal which went into the mouth, thus effectively halting her tongue. In some cases, these tongue-like protrusions were covered with sharp spikes so that if the woman moved her tongue, she suffered severe injuries. It seems that not even this cruelty was sufficient to halt some nagging tongues.

There were many varieties of brank, some of which are now held in museums or even in churches. One on display in Walton-on-Thames parish church bears the date 1632 and the verse:

> Chester presents Walton with a bridle
> To curb women's tongues that talk too idle.

In some cases, men at the receiving end of such tongues organized their own punishment for vicious wives. One example comes from the severely nagged men of Congleton in Cheshire. They installed large hooks beside their fireplaces. If their wives scolded them, they would call in the jailer, at the same time asking him to bring the town brank or scold's bridle.

The offending woman was then fastened to that hook for a few hours, being released only when she promised to curb her tongue. The last known public use of a brank occurred as recently as 1824 at Congleton when a woman called Ann Runcorn was prosecuted for scolding and using harsh language. She launched a tirade against the churchwardens and constables one Sunday morning as they toured the town emptying public houses then closing them during the church service. Ann Runcorn was found guilty and the penalty said that there and then she must 'have the town's bridle for scolding women put upon her, and that she be led by the magistrates' clerk through every street in the town as an example to all scolding women'.

In some towns, scolding women were placed in the stocks or the pillory, there for bored youths to pelt them with rotten eggs or mouldy fruit, and it may be of interest to learn that the common law offence of being a common scold remained active in England until 1967 – the Criminal Law Act of 1967 abolished it. To my knowledge, it was never used during the 1960s!

In spite of scolding being a criminal offence even while I was serving at Aidensfield, I never had occasion to place guilty ladies in the stocks or to bridle them. Even so, there were several who richly deserved some kind of preventative treatment! There were some ladies whose tongues were never still and who could deliver the most humiliating of lectures, sometimes in private and sometimes before an audience of astonished bystanders.

Before I refer to those charming examples of the female sex, I am reminded that there are some lovely words to describe such women, including shrew, spitfire, termagant, xantippe and harridan and, in spite of the punishment meted out in the past, such ladies do continue to plague us – even after death! Happily, most gentlemen can make fun of them; this occurs especially after the tongues have been stilled by death, perhaps in deep gratitude for the sudden and blessed relief that follows. For example, there is the story of a Yorkshireman whose nagging wife died. Immediately after the funeral, he was leaving the churchyard when a crack of thunder rent the air. 'Well,' he said to bystander, 'she's got there.'

In another case, this epitaph adorns a woman's tombstone at Torryburn in Scotland:

In this churchyard lies Eppie Coutts,
Either here, or somewhere hereabouts,
But where she is, none can tell
Till Eppie rise and tell hersel'.

The respite experienced by men upon the death of their nagging wives can perhaps be shown in the following epitaphs:

Here lies my wife, a sad slattern and shrew,
If I said I regretted her, I should lie too.

Underneath this sod lies Arabella Young,
Who on the 5th May began to hold her tongue.

Here snug in her grave my wife doth lie,
Now she's at rest – and so am I.

This spot is the sweetest I've seen in my life,
It raises my flowers and covers my wife.

And perhaps the shortest and most apt is upon a
Cumberland tombstone: 'Tread softly – if she wakes, she'll
talk.'

Those of us blessed with reasonable wives and female relations
may find it difficult to comprehend the power over meek
husbands which is so vociferously exercised by the harridans
to which I have referred. Men who would journey to the
frozen wastes of Siberia, who would fight for their country or
rescue drowning cats from raging floodwaters, will wilt and
quiver when confronted by a tongue-lashing from such a wife.
If the pen is mightier than the sword, then a woman's tongue
is mightier still.

I came across one of those husbands shortly after my arrival
at Aidensfield. In reflecting upon the poor fellow, I wondered
about his domestic dilemma long before I met him because he
would be seen around the village wearing a permanent
hangdog expression on his face as he did the shopping, ran
errands and confronted people on his wife's behalf whenever
she complained about anything – which was very frequently.

She was the sort of woman who would write to the television
companies or the radio if she disagreed with the content of a
programme; she seemed to think that her opinion was the only
one that mattered. She wrote to the newspapers, to women's
magazines, to the parish council, to Members of Parliament
and even to the Prime Minister, and her letters were always of
the complaining type. She never wrote to say 'thank you'. But
when it came to confronting those who, in her misguided
opinion, had wronged her, she rarely met them face to face.
She made her husband fire all her bullets. If she found a bad
potato in a sack, it was her husband who had to complain to
the grocer; if she bought new clothes and found a fault, it was
her husband who had to ring up and grumble; if the postman

was late, she made him ring the post office and even, if she objected to a television programme, it was her husband who was made to ring the BBC. She wrote to them but she made him telephone them. In short, she ordered him about until he had almost abandoned any chance of having a mind of his own.

His name was Richard Cornforth; he would be in his late forties and walked with a slight stoop, doubtless through bearing such a heavy burden all his life. His clothes always seemed to be ill-fitting, with his jackets being too long or baggy, his trousers often being worn at half-mast and shirt collars crumpled. I'm sure his wife nagged him about his appearance, but in this, he never seemed to improve. He was never dirty or scruffy; he just looked eternally crumpled.

Richard worked for a local brewery called Heather Ales whose premises were at Eltering. I was never quite sure what he did, but it was something to do with supervision of the wort as the hops were added to the brew-kettle prior to boiling, the full recipe for their beers being something of a local secret. He drove to work in a smart Ford Anglia which he polished lovingly whenever he could escape from his wife's nagging, although I had patrolled past while hearing her exhorting him to clean the ashtray, sweep the interior and make sure the windows were clean, back, front and sides. Richard was a quiet, law-abiding fellow, the sort who would excite mothering instincts in a woman rather than any sexual interest, but my links with him were few because I never had any cause to visit his home. Indeed, I kept well away.

It was a small semi-detached house on the edge of Aidensfield with a neat garden and ceramic ornaments on the interior window-ledges. Mrs Cornforth was often to be seen outside the house, polishing the windows, sweeping the paths, washing the woodwork of the doors and keeping the exterior in pristine condition. Even though I had never been into the house, it was strongly rumoured around the village that it was unbelievably immaculate inside with never a speck of dust to be seen. It was one of those houses whose contents glistened in the sunshine, but where, when the sun shone, the curtains were closed to prevent it fading the carpets and furniture and

where stair-runners covered the carpets to prevent wear and
tear.

Local legend said you could literally eat a meal off the
kitchen floor without getting the tiniest mite of dust in your
spaghetti bolognaise. It was the sort of house which 99 per
cent of all known germs never dared to visit.

Then one spring weekend, Mrs Cornforth was unexpectedly
called away to visit a sick aunt in Newcastle-upon-Tyne and,
for the first time in his married life, Richard found himself
alone. Quite unbelievably, he was left in charge of the marital
home, a situation rather like a canoeist unexpectedly finding
himself in command of the *Titanic*.

But, the truth is that in Richard's case, he was *almost* in
charge. Esme, his wife, had organized his meals, leaving notes
to tell him when to put certain casseroles in the oven and when
to eat the baked items she had left. He had to wind the
grandfather clock, feed the cat, shake the doormat and make
the bed – she'd left him little notes to jog his memory, and
secondary notes to tell him where to find the first notes. There
were additional notes too, explaining about ordering meat
from the butcher, greens from the grocery van, a pint a day
from the milkman and the best trout or plaice from the visiting
fishman. In spite of these commandments, Richard was to a
large extent left to his own devices – she hadn't told him when
to go to bed, for example, or when to get up.

What Esme hadn't bargained for, however, was that one of
Richard's nag-free nights was a Saturday. It was not an
ordinary Saturday either.

Richard, during the course of his employment, had often
heard about the masculine fun that accompanied Saturday
nights, especially when his workmates went off to watch
football or cricket and afterwards went out to the pub. He'd
heard that they went either to celebrate a win or drown their
sorrows if their team lost. Whatever the outcome, they went to
the pub and had chicken and chips in a basket, or
fish-and-chips from the chippy in Eltering High Street,
followed by a few pints.

Although Richard had been a reasonable sportsman during
his youth, he had never taken part in a sporting event since his

marriage to Esme at the ripe old age of twenty-two. It was during a conversation at work that his colleagues discovered Richard had a moment of freedom, a chance to enjoy a brief new life, something akin to the twenty hours of a mayfly's existence. Ever eager to make him happy, they lost no time persuading him to join them for a taste of bliss on that particular Saturday.

They knew he needed a good night out; *he* knew he needed a good night out and, hopefully, Esme would never know a thing about it. It was with some excitement, therefore, that on that fateful Saturday night, Richard joined the Heather Ales annual spring staff outing when it had been decided they would attend Eltering football club to witness Eltering play in the final of the Heather Ales Moors Trophy competition. This was a cup to be played for by all the market towns which surrounded the North York Moors; it was a fiercely fought competition and Eltering had never won the trophy in its 25-year history.

Now, they had a strong team which was highly fancied and they had thrashed all comers. On that Saturday, therefore, there was every chance the cup would be theirs and, as Richard's employers, Heather Ales, had donated the trophy, it seemed fitting that all the employees, or as many as possible, should witness the match and join any subsequent celebrations. Richard had agreed it was a good idea.

Eltering won by five goals to two, a resounding victory, and after the presentation of the trophy, there was a buffet supper, with drinking and dancing at The Bay Horse in Eltering. Richard, having been given a lift by a friend, was one of the packed host in that comfortable old inn. The drinks flowed, the food was good, the music was divine, the dancing was wonderful and Richard had the time of his life. His natural exuberance astonished his workmates, his sense of fun cheered them while his capacity for buying drinks warmed their hearts.

The woman with whom he danced away the evening told him he was handsome and clever, so he bought her lots of drinks and lots for himself, the result of which he felt very romantic and loving. But all too soon, the marvellous evening was over; like Cinderella, it was time for Richard to go home. By now, of course, he was broke and, worse still, he was paralytically drunk. The colleague who had given him a lift to Eltering knew he lived somewhere in Aidensfield, having picked him up at the war memorial, but did not know to which of the houses Richard belonged.

And, at that stage of the evening, Richard did not know either, or perhaps it is more truthful to say, he was unable to explain where he lived. As a consequence, he was assisted from his colleague's motor car and settled in a swaying position upon the lower steps of Aidensfield war memorial. The time was about 12.30 and it was now Sunday morning as his cheerful voice sang about Nellie Dean as well as producing some bawdy renderings of exceedingly rumbustious rugby songs. He remained on the steps of the war memorial to offer his rendition to the public but it is fair to say that the people of Aidensfield did not know the identity of the tuneless moron who was making such a din in the middle of the village, nor did they seem to appreciate the fine baritone voice which emanated from his lips. Several of them telephoned me with ardent requests for me to extinguish the racket and then to lock up the noisy crowd.

Half asleep, I crawled out of bed, put on my uniform jacket and trousers, and made my way into the centre of the village. I parked the van on the edge of the green and even above the noise of its engine, could hear the awful moaning sounds and strange music that came from the vicinity of the war memorial.

Upon my arrival, I saw that it was not a crowd, it was Richard, singing a Territorial Army camp-fire version of 'Eskimo Nell' in several different voices.

The fumes which issued from his wide-open mouth told me must have consumed half of Heather Ales' daily output of beer, and the words which came from the same place told me he had no idea who he was, where he was or what he was. He was blissfully happy – but I was not. None the less, at such an early hour of the morning, I had no wish to be faced with the awful chore of making written reports about his conduct, nor did I wish to antagonize him or his wife by arresting him for being drunk and disorderly. The simple solution was to take him home – if he continued to sing in the house, it was no concern of mine, although the neighbours might complain. The Noise Abatement Act of 1960 did make provision for those who created noise and vibration to the annoyance of the public but whether its provisions would cope with Richard's music was something I dared not anticipate at that moment.

Like most of the village, I knew that Esme was away for the weekend and for that reason, the task was less fraught than it would otherwise have been. Upon reflection, of course, if Esme had been at home, this would never have happened. However, I struggled with Richard as I manoeuvred him towards the front door of his house and I managed to find the key in his pocket. I opened the door, switched on the light and said, 'Home Richard. You're home. In you go. Mind the step.'

The rapid change in his demeanour was both astonishing and bewildering. He appeared to sober up almost immediately.

'No, Mr Rhea, I can't. I cannot go in, I must not go in.'

'But, Richard,' I was puzzled, 'This is your house, isn't it? I've got the right place? The key fits . . . .'

'Yes, Mr Rhea, yes indeed it is, but . . . .'

'She's away, Richard, Esme's away, I can take you in . . . .'

'Good heavens no, Mr Rhea, my word, no. Not at all, no. I must not go in.'

I propped him against the door pillar, shouted Esme's name and then said, 'See, she's not there, the coast is clear.'

'I'll stay out, Mr Rhea, in the garage, in my car, that will solve matters, no trouble there, no trouble at all . . . .'

'Look, what on earth's the matter? I can't leave you out here, you're in no fit state and besides, if you stay here you'll freeze or you'll start singing again, and no one can abide the noises you make. So come on, in you go,' and I took his arm.

He pulled free, saying, 'No, I can't, Mr Rhea, no, not now . . . .'

'But why?' I shouted at him. 'Why won't you go in?'

'I haven't got my slippers on,' he said quietly. 'Esme says I must always put my slippers on before I enter the house, the floors, you see, they're all highly polished . . . .'

'Then take your shoes off,' I suggested.

'No, Esme says sweaty feet make marks on the polished floors, Mr Rhea . . . .'

'Where are your slippers?' I asked.

'In a box outside the back door,' he said.

'You're joking!'

'No, Mr Rhea, I'm not.' His voice remained slurred during these exchanges, but the threat of Esme had indeed driven most of the drunken influences from his body. I supported him as he panted and puffed along the path at the side of the house and eventually we came to what appeared to be a dog-kennel. It was outside the back door and I shone my pocket-torch inside; a pair of man's slippers waited for their owner's homecoming.

'Put them on,' I said.

He obeyed. Now he was at home, he would obey my orders, just as if I was Esme. Sitting on the back doorstep, he managed to remove his shoes and replaced them with his slippers whereupon I said, 'Right, in we go. Back to the front door.'

'Not the front door, Mr Rhea. I'm never allowed to use the front door, that's only for funerals and weddings.'

'Then we'll use this door, the back door.'

'I didn't bring the key, I took the front door key by mistake, Mr Rhea, and I can't go in there, not now . . . .'

'Wait there,' I said sharply.

I went into the house via the front door, leaving a mud trail along the gleaming passage which led into the kitchen, then I padded across a shining white-tiled kitchen floor to the back door. I unlocked it, opened it wide and said to Richard, 'There, we've solved that one. In you come, Richard.'

'Thank you Mr Rhea.' He seemed most relieved. 'Thank you . . . now, what can I tell Esme, about tonight . . . .'

'Nothing,' I said. 'You tell her absolutely nothing.'

'But she'll know . . . .'

'Not if you clean those footmarks off the hall and kitchen floor.' I pointed to my own marks. 'That can be your punishment for coming home in this condition. I'll not say a word!'

He smiled and closed the door as I left.

But as I walked away, I heard a woman's voice from upstairs crying, 'Richard? Is that you? Where have you been? I want an answer, Richard, I want an answer this minute, I'm coming down . . . .'

I left hurriedly. Esme had returned just as unexpectedly as she had departed, and as I had no wish to be on the receiving end of her tongue-lashing, I scurried away. As I trotted to my waiting van, I saw the door of Richard's house burst open as he also fled into the sheltering darkness of the night. Then I lost him. I have no idea where he spent that night, but wherever it was, he remained silent, perhaps knowing that if he sang, Esme would find him.

I do not know what transpired between him and Esme after his brief taste of freedom but he did appear to join more events in the village and his confidence increased. He even bought me a pint of beer in the pub one night.

Another bossy wife came to my notice when a hiker reported finding some stolen property, namely a bottle of Scotch whisky, hidden in a cavity in a dry stone wall.

The wall runs along the side of the lane in Rannockdale, a remote dale which contains a scattering of farms and lonely stone-built cottages. It is an ancient wall and was then in a tumbledown condition with many large holes within its length. It was hardly the place to be patronized by thieves or disposers of stolen goods, but the bottle of whisky was new and unopened. The fact that it had been thrust deep into the cavity suggested it had been hidden there, so it could hardly be classified as lost property. Some furtiveness had been involved; skulduggery was suspected.

'You'd better keep observations on that wall, Rhea,' ordered Sergeant Blaketon. 'It sounds to me like the sort of thing that Claude Jeremiah Greengrass would do. If he, or anybody else, is dumping stolen goods on your patch, it could mean somebody's coming out to collect them. A hotbed of receivers, Rhea, a nest of felons under your very nose, so you've got to nip this crime ring in the bud, eh? You've got to arrest them. And if it is Greengrass, I want him inside. Right?'

'Yes, Sergeant,' I said, knowing that if Greengrass had stolen the whisky, it would have been drunk long ago; Claude would never risk leaving any of his treasures for others to enjoy. So began a long, fruitless period of keeping unproductive observations on the activities of Claude Jeremiah and also upon a length of dry stone wall some three miles long by six feet high.

The problem was that other valuables were later found hidden in various parts of that wall and I felt sure Greengrass was not responsible. Somehow, they were always placed there while I was not keeping watch, but having said that, it is difficult keeping a simultaneous watch on every hole in a wall of that length. To achieve that degree of observation, a posse of constables would be required to keep watch for twenty-four hours a day, seven days a week.

Over the following weeks, visitors, local people, farmers, shepherds and ramblers came to me with things they had found in the wall – a bottle of sherry, a pack of 200 cigarettes, a shot pheasant, several boxes of chocolates, a hardback novel, some bottles of beer, tins of fruit, packages of butter and margarine, jars of jam and marmalade . . . .

From time to time in my years at Aidensfield, I'd had reports of sneak thieves, people who enter houses through unlocked doors to steal the first thing that they see, such as a radio set in the kitchen, the butcher's money or a nice vase. Also, from time to time, I'd seen Alfred, Claude Jeremiah Greengrass's lurcher, mooching about the streets; sometimes he had a slab of wrapped butter in his mouth or a teacake or, more likely, a mutton chop, a chicken leg or a joint of roast beef. Alfred was in fact responsible for a lot of unreported crime in Aidensfield, but I did not think the dog or its master had taken to hiding goodies in a dry stone wall. Sergeant Blaketon was not convinced, however.

'I can't totally accept that Greengrass is not the culprit. I'll bet he's behind this, so have you spoken to the local shopkeepers, Rhea?' asked Sergeant Blaketon one afternoon. 'This is mainly the sort of stuff anyone can buy from village shops. Or nick from kitchen tables. That dog of his is a four-legged crime wave. Has Greengrass become a shoplifter and has that bloody dog of his been learning lessons from squirrels? Hiding things like this . . . .'

'I don't think so,' I confirmed. 'I've had words with them all, but they've not been raided, nothing like this has been stolen. They all know Claude Jeremiah well enough to keep an eye on him, but he's no shoplifter, Sergeant. I've had no reports of break ins at shops or houses either, so I doubt if this is stolen property after all. It's more like someone just getting rid of it . . . .'

'Why would they do that? It's all good quality stuff, it's not rotten or condemned, is it?'

'And it's brand names, Sergeant,' I said. 'Good stuff.'

'Exactly, it's just the sort of daft game Greengrass would play. It's definitely a Greengrass sort of going-on if you ask me, Rhea,' he sighed. 'Well, keep at it.'

Then one Monday morning, I was in Joe Steel's shop when a rambler hailed me. He was in his sixties and warmly clad in hiking gear.

'Ah, Constable,' he said, producing a tin of peaches from his anorak pocket. 'I found this, I thought I'd better hand it in. It was hidden in the dry stone in Rannockdale, near the footpath to Flossie's Foss. I wondered if there'd been a raid, it hasn't been there long, the tin's not rusty or anything.'

Flossie's Foss was a local waterfall, foss being a local word for a high waterfall along a beck or stream. I thanked him and explained what was happening so far as hidden goods were concerned, took his name and gave him a receipt.

When he'd left the shop, Joe said, 'I gave that tin for the village hall raffle, Nick, last week. I'm sure it's the same one, I recognize the dent in the side.'

'That dent wasn't made by Alfred's teeth, was it?' I asked.

'No, it got damaged in transit. That's why I thought it was a good raffle prize, I'd have had some small difficulty selling it.'

He examined it more closely and confirmed that it was indeed the very same raffle prize he had donated.

'Have you given other things for raffle prizes recently?' I asked and I then listed some of the found articles. When he said they *all* sounded like raffle prizes, I went home and checked the dates of events at the village hall. Almost invariably, there had been an event in the hall shortly before the discovery of the hidden articles. But why would anyone conceal a raffle prize in a dry stone wall miles from anywhere?

I decided to keep discreet observations in the vicinity of the village hall during the course of the next function. The first event during my new strategy was a whist drive in aid of Rannockdale village hall funds, and there was to be a raffle. I decided to patrol the village that evening and, on the pretext of wishing to buy a raffle ticket, I went into the hall just before the drive started and bought a full book of tickets whilst eyeing the choice of prizes. There was the usual stuff – a leg of ham, a pound of sausages, tins of fruit, vegetables, bottles of whisky, rum, gin and sherry, some bottles of beer, a box of chocolates, some soap and perfume and sundry other worthy prizes.

As I strode out of the hall clutching my tickets, I tried to memorize the names of everyone present – it wasn't easy, but among the fifty or so faces I did notice the whiskered features of Don Ledger. In his early fifties, he sported a huge grey moustache which seemed to wrap itself around his cheeks in large curls and thus he was recognizable in any crowd.

Don was prominent in my mind for further reasons because (a) he was a very staunch supporter of anything that happened in Rannockdale village hall and (b) he lived in Rannockdale. He worked Peat Hag Farm which was a small hill farm providing a very modest income from a large flock of moorland sheep and a few sturdy beasts, some Scottish Highland cattle being among them. His farm was at the top of the dale, at the far extremity of that dry stone wall.

Another of his quirks was that he never drove anywhere, having never passed a driving test; his wife did drive and she would sometimes drive over to Whitby or Eltering to do her shopping, but Don always walked.

I decided he was the man to watch.

The raffle was drawn at the interval, but no one left the hall until the end of the whist drive, and I made sure I was concealed in the darkness as the players departed. Sure enough, Don emerged and I saw he was carrying a bottle of gin. It was cradled in his arm like a baby. As he said his farewells and began the long walk back to Peat Hag Farm, I remained in the shadows and began to follow him. I was wearing my crêpe-soled boots – these were known as Brothel Creepers within the police service because they enabled us to move in total silence. And so I began a long walk, always maintaining a safe distance behind Don by making full use of shadows cast by trees, houses, haystacks and the dry stone wall itself. And then, as Don approached a stile which formed part of a public footpath across the dale, I saw him stoop against the wall.

I heard the sound of glass against stone and knew he was concealing the bottle of gin. I waited until he was out of sight and earshot, then recovered the bottle from a hole in the wall. Sure enough, it was the bottle which had been a raffle prize earlier that evening; the counterfoil of the winning ticket was still stuck to it. I decided to take it back to the police house with a view to paying Don a visit tomorrow.

Next morning, I rang Peat Hag Farm and Mrs Ledger answered.

'It's PC Rhea,' I announced. 'I thought I'd come out and sign Don's stock registers this morning about elevenish. I wanted to check he was in before I drove over to Rannockdale.'

'He'll be in,' her response was short almost to the point of curtness. 'I won't, I'm going shopping to Eltering. I'll tell him to expect you, I'll leave the 'lowance out ready.'

Before leaving, I placed all the recovered items in a box in the police van and when I arrived, I found Don pointing a wall to one of his outbuildings and he welcomed me, inviting me into the spacious kitchen where, as promised, Mrs Ledger had left out some scones and cakes. Don made a pot of coffee and we settled down for our 'lowance, as the midmorning coffee break is called hereabouts.

Following the introductory chatter about nothing in particular, I checked and signed his stock registers, then decided to ask about the raffle prizes.

'Don,' I began somewhat tentatively, 'In the back of my van, I've got a box full of groceries, drinks and things. Raffle prizes, I believe.'

'Won summat, have you?' he smiled with just a hint of guile.

'Not me, it's not often I win raffles,' I told him. 'No, these are odds and ends folk have handed to me in recent weeks, folks like hikers, ramblers, passers-by and so on. Very honest folks I might add. The stuff was found in holes along the length of a dry stone wall, the wall that runs up Rannockdale almost to this farm; when we got the stuff handed to us, naturally we thought somebody was hiding stolen goods, Don, but now I know different. It's not stolen, it's not the proceeds of crime. It's raffle prizes. I reckon the stuff belongs to you.'

'Aye, it does, all on it, ivvery bit,' he said without hesitation. 'Cheeky buggers, eh? Nicking my stuff . . . .'

'They wouldn't know it was yours, Don,' I said. 'I mean, to find a whole bottle of whisky or a pack of 200 cigarettes in a hole in a wall is quite a discovery. So it can't have been all that well hidden. So they're yours, eh?'

'Aye, and Ah know what you're going to ask next,' he laughed. 'Why did Ah felt it like that?'

'Exactly,' I said, knowing that 'felt' is an old Yorkshire word for 'hide'.

'It's t'wife,' he grinned. 'She was brung up as a strict Wesleyan, an' there's nowt wrang wi' that, but she dissn't like gambling. She hates me buying raffle tickets, thoo sees, Mr Rhea, she counts that as gambling, but, well, 'cos Ah'm a big supporter o' t'village hall, Ah likes to pay my whack. So Ah maks sure Ah allus gits a ticket or two. T'snag is, Mr Rhea, Ah wins ivvery tahme. Ah can fair guarantee Ah'll win summat.'

'I don't, I buy hundreds of tickets and rarely win anything!' I grumbled.

'Well, mebbe Ah's got somebody caring for me from above, so Ah dissn't like refusing and Ah can't give 'em away late at night, so that's why Ah felt yon things, nut very well it seems. It's so as t'wife nivver sets eyes on 'em.'

'But if you hide them like that, you must intend to retrieve them later?'

'Oh aye. Ah gives 'em all away, fresh raffle prizes, them that's not takken bi other fooalks, and Ah gives 'em ti t'awd folks, needy families, hospitals, that sooart o' thing. Yon bits was nivver there very lang afoor Ah gat rid on 'em, Mr Rhea. Usually Ah'd given 'em ti somebody within a day or two.'

'But you must have wondered where they were going? Those that disappeared?'

'Nay, nut really. There's mair tourists aboot these days so it's a fair bet some o' them things'd be found. And that dissn't worry me, Mr Rhea, if they're gahin ti help some deserving case. Ah mean, Ah deearn't want them things, so other folks might as well 'ave t'use of 'em. That's way Ah sees things, Mr Rhea. Onnybody that taks things Ah've felted is welcome tiv 'em.'

'It's very kind of you, Don.' I had to admire him. 'It's very generous. So, I've got a box full of things in my van, what shall I do with them?'

'What aboot t'Orthopaedic at Brantsford? Dis thoo ivver git doon there?'

'My wife's doing some voluntary work there, on a part-time basis,' I said. 'It keeps her up-to-date with medical matters and she loves working with the patients. So, yes, she can take the things to them, they'll be welcomed.'

'Right. Thoo'll nut tell oor missus?'

'No,' I assured him.

'Then t'matter's owered. More 'lowance, Mr Rhea?'

'I wouldn't say no to another of those scones,' I said as he refilled my mug.

Perhaps the most impressive indication of the power of a woman over a man was revealed to myself and the other constables of Ashfordly Section when Mrs Blaketon refused to let Sergeant Oscar Blaketon watch the Cup Final.

When the inspector at Eltering arranged our duties for that auspicious day, Sergeant Blaketon found himself quivering with frustration and disbelief. He had been put on duty on the afternoon of Cup Final day and there was no other supervisory officer on duty with whom he could exchange shifts. It was 1965, the year that Liverpool played Leeds – and Sergeant Blaketon was a staunch Leeds supporter.

Once his initial anger had subsided, he had promised himself that, whatever happened, he would not miss the match. He would watch it on television.

As he made his plans, there is no doubt that Sergeant Blaketon was very suspicious about the way the duties had been allocated by the inspector – he knew the inspector was himself a keen soccer supporter as was Sergeant Bairstow and the other sergeants at Eltering. Poor old Oscar guessed there had been some collusion in fixing their duties so they would not miss the match. The fact they had all gone to Wembley on the same bus trip did add some weight to his suspicions.

But in spite of the gloom, there was a slight glimmer of hope. Sergeant Blaketon's responsibility that day, in the absence of the others, was Cover Duty. That meant he was on call for the entire day – he was allowed to take time off in between parts of his shift as long as he was always available. He reasoned that if he worked that morning and evening, he could have the afternoon at home; if he sat at home that Saturday afternoon to watch the Cup Final, then he would be on call within easy reach of the telephone and therefore available to attend to any occurrence. Once he'd overcome his initial disappointment, he did seem happy to go along with that arrangement and I knew he would pray to his favourite god there was no call-out incident of any kind during the match.

But a major problem did arise. It was one he had never foreseen. There was an old romantic film on the other channel that same afternoon, a real Hollywood weepie; it was a blockbusting tear-jerking drama of world-wide appeal, one which produced floods of tears among the world's women.

And, for the life of me, I can't remember its title.

However, Oscar Blaketon's blissful dream came to an end when Mrs Blaketon announced she had invited some friends around for the afternoon to view the weepie; tea would be served between bouts of tears, crumpets would help to appease the agony of thwarted love, beating hearts might even be assuaged with a glass or two of sherry and, all in all, the lovelorn ladies of Ashfordly were determined to have a marvellously sad time enriched with Mrs Blaketon's hospitality amid severely alternating bouts of tender emotion and fiery passion. Their desires marked the effective end of Oscar Blaketon's Cup dream.

By chance, I had popped into Ashfordly police station to leave some correspondence and was in the office just when this news had been presented to Blaketon by his wife. I could hear him pleading with her; through the door which linked his house to the police office, I could hear his desperate voice pleading with her to view the film at the house of another of the invited women. Mrs Blaketon steadfastly refused.

'Don't be silly, Oscar,' she retorted. 'Their husbands are all watching the Cup Final. You can't watch it, you're working so that's why we decided to watch the film here. They can watch their silly football in peace while we're all here.'

I could hear his pleas as he said, 'The husbands could all go to one of the other men's houses, there'd be a spare set if they did that; you could all go to that house, the one with the spare set.'

'Our arrangements have been made, Oscar,' she said.

'But,' he persisted, 'I'm sure some of the men will be viewing together, you know, with a few bottles of beer. There's bound to be an empty house or two. If you found out which house was empty, you and your ladies could all go there, and then that would leave our television free for me . . . .'

'No, we can't do that, their friends aren't the same as our friends, some of the men are having their own friends in, from different families. It's not at all easy, Oscar, arranging social get-togethers like this. It's impossible to change things now, everyone's made their arrangements. I've made my plans for eats and drinks, I'm not changing anything, not now, it's too late. So that's final. No more arguments. Besides, you're on duty that afternoon so I can't see why you are making such a fuss.'

'But I want to watch the Cup Final,' he pleaded. 'I'm on cover all day, I'll be on call. I just need to be near a telephone. I can take time off at home, you see, but I can't go to some other house like they can. Surely, you could make some changes in your arrangements, just for me, just this once; those men and women are not on call, you're not on call, you don't have to sit near your telephone in case of a call-out . . . .'

'I have made my arrangements, Oscar, and I am not going to change them. I've already told you that. And that's final.'

When I heard his footsteps approaching the door, I busied myself with some papers and watched his unhappy return. His face said everything; it oozed misery.

'Something wrong, Sergeant?' I ventured.

'Women, Rhea! That's what's wrong. Women. Fancy wanting to watch a nauseating old romantic film instead of the year's most famous football match. And it's Leeds and Liverpool . . . silly old cow . . .' and he went into his office.

When I looked at the duty rota, which was made up a fortnight in advance, I saw that I was off duty on Cup Final day. It was my long weekend off, i.e. Friday through to Sunday inclusive, which meant I could view the game on television; had I wished and had I known in advance, I could even have gone to Wembley to watch it live. But I am not a particularly keen football fan and have rarely, if ever, watched a match. But I enjoy the Cup Final and always try to watch it, just as I watch the Grand National, the Derby, the Boat Race and other major sporting events. And so I decided that I would watch the match.

And because I would be off duty and free to watch the game, I knew what would happen. Whoever was patrolling the area on duty would find a reason to visit my police house while the match was in progress . . . and so I did expect an influx of one or two officers; somehow, they would wangle a visit. At least one officer would be patrolling in the Eltering subdivision and another would be touring the Brantsford area.

From Ashfordly Section, there would be Phil Bellamy. Phil would surely arrive, for I saw he'd been allocated a 2 p.m.–10 p.m. duty that afternoon and he was a keen soccer fan. But Bellamy's duty was not a cover duty and so he should not officially sneak time off to watch football – but if he did, he should take care not be caught doing so. I've no doubt he banked on Blaketon's own desire to see the match – if Blaketon was watching the Cup Final, he would not be out on patrol, trying to catch young officers skiving off duty!

In the days following my discovery of Blaketon's predicament, I began to notice that he was very considerate towards me, more so than usual; he would chat for longer periods in a very friendly manner, he would say that if I ever had problems, I should not be afraid to ask for his advice or help. Then, on the Thursday evening he met me at nine o'clock. I was due to go off duty at ten.

'A thought's just occurred to me, Rhea,' he smiled; I thought it was a rather devious smile.

'Yes, Sergeant?'

'My wife and her friends are viewing a corny old romantic film on Saturday afternoon. Would Mrs Rhea like to join them? I'm sure I could arrange it.'

'Saturday? No, thanks, Sergeant, I think we'll be going shopping,' I said, having already guessed his intentions.

'Oh, well, I just thought she might like an outing . . . .'

'She's not really into old tear-jerkers,' I smiled.

'But you're off duty tomorrow as well, eh? You know, Rhea, whenever I had a Friday off, I liked to get my weekend chores done on the Friday, then I had the Saturday clear. The shops aren't so busy on Fridays, you can get parked easier than Saturdays . . . Fridays are a very good day for shopping, Rhea. You ought to try it sometimes, I really think you'd enjoy shopping on a Friday.'

'Yes, but some of our children are at school, you see, so we're tied to weekends . . . .'

'Oh,' he said, obviously not appreciating the dictates of a family with tiny children. 'I like going to watch Leeds, you see . . . .' I don't think he was listening to me now. 'Do you know they're in the Cup Final this year? Playing Liverpool? At Wembley?'

'No, I had no idea,' I lied. 'It should be a good match. Are you going to see them? Isn't there a bus trip down to Wembley from Eltering? I heard the inspector was going.'

'Yes,' he said. 'But sadly my duties didn't work out in my favour, I'm on call that day. I'm hoping to see it on television though. It's live coverage.'

'Oh, that'll be exciting,' I beamed at him. 'But I'm no football fan. Cricket yes, because that's a Yorkshireman's game, but apart from that, I'm not much of a sports fan.'

'You won't be watching the match then?' I knew he was

struggling to induce me into offering him an invitation to view it, but he did not wish to make an overt request.

'I'm not sure, I might watch,' I said flippantly. 'If I can get Mary and the kids out to the shops and back again before kick-off, then I'll watch. But I'm not going to break my neck to rush home just to view some footballers. Besides,' I added, 'it's not easy watching television with four little children galloping about the room.'

He went away with his problem unresolved and I heard later that he'd mentioned the match to the other constables who would be on duty that afternoon. As in my case, he had never made a direct request to watch the match on their televisions, but his intentions had been very clear. Poor old Oscar . . . .

I must admit I began to feel sorry for him because his dilemma became a subject of fun among the constables; they were all determined to make him miss the match.

In my own case, I had no intention of going shopping with Mary and the children; she and her friends had decided to have a joint expedition to York, leaving all the multitude of several families' children with a nursery minder, and thus making available the television sets for the whims of their husbands. Thus I had my own set all to myself. I decided to obtain a few bottles of beer, some crisps and a pork pie and then to savour the atmosphere of the game with whichever of my colleagues managed to arrive.

At 2.30 that Saturday afternoon, as the TV set was warming up with pre-match scenes from the ground, my telephone rang. It was Phil Bellamy.

'Nick,' he said. 'I'm ringing from the kiosk in Aidensfield. Any chance of a coffee? I'm on a job on your patch, report of an escaped prisoner, I thought I'd call in . . . .'

'Escaped prisoner? That's a likely tale! You mean you want to watch the Cup Final?' I laughed.

'Well, if it happens to be on when I'm there . . . .'

'Sure,' I said. 'Drop in.'

By three minutes to three, Phil and two motor patrol constables from Strensford were settled on our settee each with a mug of coffee as the excitement at Wembley rose to a crescendo and then, as the moment of kick-off approached, the doorbell rang.

'Pretend you're out!' shouted Phil.

'I'm not on duty,' I retorted. 'You are. So if it's a job, it's yours, mate! Besides, we can't ignore it, your police car's outside and there's a patrol car beside it. It's like a police road traffic department out there . . . .'

He groaned as he anticipated an urgent request for his attention, but when I opened the door, Sergeant Blaketon was standing there in full uniform. And he was smiling broadly.

'Good heavens, Sergeant,' I said, in what I hoped was a voice loud enough for Phil and the others to hear, 'Whatever brings you out to Aidensfield when I'm off duty?'

'I just happened to be passing,' he said and I could see the glint of success in his eye.

'Really?' I detected facetiousness in his voice.

'Yes. And I saw Bellamy's car. And that patrol car, both parked outside. I wondered if they'd had any success tracing that escaped prisoner?'

'What escaped prisoner?' I asked. Had there really been an escapee in Aidensfield? I hadn't heard anything about it.

'You won't have heard, you're off duty but, well, I knew you wouldn't mind if I called in, seeing we're all in this together, this search; I know you're not on duty . . . .'

The crafty old schemer had come out deliberately, I knew; he'd known I'd be at home, he'd known Mary would be out and I bet he knew Bellamy would be here too, sneaking time off to watch the Final . . . .

'Fancy a coffee, Sergeant?' I asked.

'Not interrupting anything, am I?' he grinned.

'I've just made one for Phil and the others,' I said. 'They all had a job on my patch, they were all looking for that prisoner . . . .'

'Were they now? And have they obtained any sightings?' asked Sergeant Blaketon.

'I've no idea, Sergeant, they haven't said.'

Then, from the living-room, I heard the roar of the crowd as the teams ran on to the pitch. Blaketon heard it and I saw the reaction. He was itching to get in there and watch.

'Watching telly, are we, Rhea?'

'My wife's gone out, the children are being looked after, so I thought I'd watch the telly. It's Cup Final day, Sergeant,' I said as if I wasn't really interested. 'Leeds versus Liverpool.'

'Is it really?'

'Would you like to join us? The kettle's boiled . . . .'

But before I could say anything else, Oscar Blaketon was rushing through to my lounge, removing his cup in the process, and he was just in time to flop into a chair as the whistle blew for kick-off. I heard him say, 'Not a word, Bellamy, not one word,' as he fixed his gaze on the screen.

I took in a coffee for him, with one for myself and a second one for Phil and the others who sat just as transfixed as Sergeant Blaketon as they barely acknowledged my presence. Their addiction was complete. And so Phil and the patrol officers remained to watch the game; no other constables called to watch the game – Blaketon's car, parked outside, would have warned them off if they had made an approach – but had they known, they could have come in. Oscar was in his seventh heaven as he savoured every kick on Wembley's turf, but when Liverpool won by two goals to one, he left quietly, if a little sad. It hadn't been the dream result he'd desired.

'Thank you, Rhea,' he said as he left. 'Anything to report, Bellamy?' He turned to Phil with a look of dejection on his face.

'I think that report about an escaped prisoner must have been a false alarm, Sergeant,' Phil said. 'I can't find anyone resembling an escapee, nor anyone who made the report. You said a lady had called you from Aidensfield?'

'We heard your call to PC Bellamy on the air, Sergeant,' said one of the patrol officers. 'We were nearby, so we decided to patrol the village, just in case.'

'I thought there might just be time to make a search before kick-off,' grinned Blaketon.

'Yes, there was,' said Bellamy.

'And, as I'm on cover duty, I thought I'd better attend myself just in case it was a genuine call. You never can tell with calls like that,' he said with a strange smile on his face.

But when I checked the Occurrence Book later, there was

no entry about the reported sighting of an escaped prisoner. No one had rung in to report one. I decided that Sergeant Blaketon had been very cunning on that occasion. He had scored points over his wife too, for she never knew he had seen the match and neither Phil nor I would tell her.

5 *Taking Care of the Pennies*

The unsunned heaps of miser's treasures.
John Milton (1608–74)

Most of us associate the word 'miser' with a man who greedily hoards his money but I cannot find a feminine equivalent of that word. One of my dictionaries fails to provide any hint as to the sex of a miser, but says that it means one who hoards wealth and lives miserably; an avaricious person. Another says the word means one who deprives *himself* of all but the barest essentials in order to hoard money. From this latter definition, one might be tempted to believe there are no female misers but in the course of my duties at Aidensfield, I did come across certain women whose behaviour might well have qualified them as miserly.

One such lady suffered a sudden and mysterious death. Her name was Adelaide Bowes, she was unmarried and she lived alone in a ramshackle cottage in Undercliffe Road. She presented a strange sight as she trudged around Aidensfield in an old brown longcoat dating to World War I, a dark headscarf which almost concealed her face and ancient wellington boots turned down at the top. Stooped and grey-haired, her age was indeterminate and the villagers said she had always looked like that; no living person could recall her appearance being any different.

Everyone considered her to be very, very poor. She bought only the most meagre of supplies from the shop, barely enough to maintain a baby let alone a full grown woman, and she never spent money on clothes or household effects. Her furniture was scrap recovered from the village tip, her house

had no electricity and no running water; she relied on an open
fire for heat, light and cooking upon, and she obtained water
from a stream which flowed past her house to join Aidensfield
Beck. Most of her time was spent wandering around the village
collecting wood for her fire and even inspecting dustbins for the
cast-offs discarded by those supposedly more wealthy. Those
cast-offs could be clothes, shoes or even food. Miss Bowes was a
recluse who shunned the friendship of everyone; no one ever
went into her house and she never visited anyone in
Aidensfield. She rarely washed, if the blackness of her hands
was any guide to the rest of her, nor did she launder her clothes
or clean the house.

As the local constable, I became aware of her shortly after my
arrival, but enquiries from several villagers assured me that she
was not in need of professional help or advice, and that she had
lived in that manner for as long as anyone knew. Sometimes, if I
bade 'good morning' to Adelaide, she would respond with a nod
of her head or even a toothless smile, but she would never allow
me to get into conversation with her.

As one of the village eccentrics, she was accepted by all and
no one tried to interfere with her life style.

Then she was missed.

It was Joe Steel who first mentioned it to me.

'Adelaide didn't come into the shop this morning,' he said to
me. 'I save old newspapers for her, she uses them to light the
fire, I think,' he added.

'Is it unusual for her not to call?' I asked.

'Fairly,' he nodded. 'She's usually pretty consistent in her
movements; it's coolish weather and she likes her papers.'

'I'll have a look at the house,' I assured him.

It was really a hovel. She owned the cottage, having inherited
it from her family, and it stood alone in a patch of overgrown
garden. There was a garden shed made of creosoted timber but
it was falling down, and the path to her front door was
overgrown with nettles and briars. The windows hadn't been
cleaned for years, the paintwork of the house was peeling off
and the woodwork was rotten. It did not look like a house which
had an occupant. When I reached the front door, I knocked
loudly and shouted, 'Adelaide? It's PC Rhea. Are you there?'

There was no reply. Not a sound came from within.

'Adelaide?' I tried the door handle; the door opened, scraping across the stone-flagged floor as I pushed it wide enough to enter. 'Adelaide? Anyone there?'

Calling my name, I climbed over the sacks of rubbish in the entrance hall, moved an old dining-chair and managed to get into the living-room.

It was full of books; they were stacked on the floor, the table, the window-ledges, the tops of cupboards – in fact, every flat surface contained several piles of books. And there were more books piled upon the piles, some neatly, others in a muddle and many in irregular heaps. I scrambled across them, climbing over lofty piles as I called her name. Some spun away beneath my feet but did not go far, as there was nowhere for them to go. It was like clambering through a heap of waste comprised entirely of old books – I bet some of them were rare editions and probably worth a fortune.

I reached the kitchen, or scullery as it is known hereabouts, but there was no sign of Adelaide. The kitchen was similarly awful, a depository for dirty crockery and pans which had never been cleaned. There were scraps of waste food, half-eaten tins of beans, half loaves of bread going mouldy . . . it was almost impossible to believe that anyone actually lived here.

Shouting the whole time, I made my way up the bare wooden staircase; it was so narrow that I walked sideways and the stench was awful. But I found Adelaide. She was lying on the bedroom floor, fully clothed in her old brown longcoat, headscarf and wellingtons, and she was clutching a tin of weedkiller. I crouched at her side, doing my best to ignore the appalling stench and touched her head. She was dead; of that there was no doubt. I guessed she had died from natural causes, but that tin of weedkiller did make me just a little concerned – had she consumed any of it? Was this a suicide?

I made a brief examination to satisfy myself that there were no signs of attack upon her and then left the house, knowing better than to touch or move anything. My first job was to call Dr Ferrenby to certify the death but if he could not ascertain the cause of death, then there would have to be a post-mortem examination. In particular, we had to satisfy ourselves whether her death was from natural causes, or whether it had happened by her own hand or by some other means.

Dr Ferrenby came directly from his surgery.

'Poor old Adelaide,' he said as he gazed upon her lifeless remains. 'What a miserable life she had. Yes, Nick, she's dead. I'll certify that. But I can't certify the cause of death, you'll need a P.M. I don't like the look of that weedkiller. It's not a murder though. Felo de se, you think?'

He used an old term for a suicide, a legal term meaning felon of one's self, or unlawful death by one's own hand. In the old days, a felo de se forfeited all his or her property and was given an ignominious burial in unconsecrated ground.

'Would it kill her?' I asked.

'Depends what's in it, you'll have to get the contents of the tin analysed. So there you are, Nick, old son; a sudden death for you to deal with.'

I radioed Sergeant Blaketon to inform him of the sudden death and to express an opinion, backed by the doctor, that there were no suspicious circumstances. I said it looked like natural causes, although suicide was just a possibility.

I then asked Sergeant Blaketon if he would arrange the despatch of the shell in a van from Eltering police station. The shell is really a makeshift coffin which is used to carry away bodies in such cases, for the corpse needed to be removed to a mortuary as soon as possible.

He said he would arrange that and added, 'If it's suicide, Rhea, she might have left a note. Lots of 'em do, you know. You'd better search the house to see if you can find one.'

I did not relish that task. To search for a suicide note among such a mass of accumulated filth threatened to be a most awesome and horrible task, but it had to be done. I returned to the house, with the body still upstairs, as I began my hunt.

I found a writing bureau in a back bedroom. It contained a writing pad and envelopes and so I started there. I found no suicide note, but I did find a handwritten will, signed by Adelaide and correctly witnessed by two people, one of whom was a solicitor. The will was simply phrased and as I read it, I saw that she had no family or relations and had left all her wealth and possessions to the Salvation Army 'in appreciation of the time you cared for me in London in 1949'. A Salvation Army captain at Eltering had been nominated as executor of her will. I wondered what they would do with all this rubbish, although the old cottage might have some value.

Then on a shelf above there was a Bible and so I decided to see if she'd placed a note within its pages – I had known that sort of thing to happen in some suicide cases.

But I was astonished at what I found. Between almost every page there was either a £1 note or a ten shilling note; as I turned the pages, the Bible revealed a fortune. I looked in some other books – and there was more accumulated wealth, hundreds and thousands of pounds. I stopped and radioed for Sergeant Blaketon to visit me urgently at the cottage. I must have a witness for this; I had no wish to be accused of helping myself to any of this hoard and so I locked the doors and waited outside. In the police service, one is always open to accusations of taking property from houses in such circumstances. It is an accusation easy to make and difficult to refute.

'What's going on, Rhea?' Sergeant Blaketon demanded as he climbed from his car half an hour later. 'Why are you standing outside the house?'

I told him, and as I was explaining, the van with the shell arrived. Before dealing with the money, we removed the body and then Blaketon and I went back inside, with me showing him the hoard of cash.

'How much more is there?' he asked, looking around the rooms and wilting at the sight of the pile of books in the living-room. I went to one of them and opened it – its pages were lined with £1 notes. I opened another – it was the same, sometimes with £1 notes and sometimes containing ten shilling notes and even fivers in some cases.

'There's thousands, Sergeant,' I said. 'Thousands.'

'We can't leave this lot unguarded, Rhea,' he said. 'What the hell can we do with it? It'll need a furniture van to shift it and besides, it's not really our problem, is it? Hasn't she any relations who'll see to it?'

I told him about the lack of relatives and of the will I'd

discovered and he smiled. 'Then let's ring the Sally Army, shall we? This must all belong to them now, the house and its contents, and that executor she's named can take charge. They can do the search, Rhea; they'll be looking for money, not a suicide note. If they find one, ask them to hand it to you, although I reckon she died naturally. She looked natural, if you know what I mean. Anyway, you'd better remain on guard, I'll get PC Rogers at Eltering to contact that Salvation Army officer named in the will, and ask him and his team to come here immediately. But you'll have to stay on guard until they are in possession of their inheritance and I think I'll get the duty solicitor to come along as well, just to make sure we've done the right thing.'

The alternative was for us to empty the house and place the entire contents in police premises for safe-keeping, but that demanded manpower and time, two things in very short supply. I thought Blaketon's solution was a good one. He had enough trust in me to leave me alone with all that cash and while I was waiting for the Salvation Army to arrive I radioed Ashfordly police station to ask Phil Bellamy to arrange for the body to be taken to the pathology lab at Scarborough Hospital.

When Captain Rodney Blair arrived in his Salvation Army uniform, I explained what lay inside the premises and he said he knew Adelaide fairly well; she had often written to him and had great respect for the Army and its work following some unspecified assistance in London years ago. I formally handed over the house and contents to him and his fellow officers, then left the premises.

My next task would be to attend the post-mortem, probably sometime tomorrow, and one of the worst jobs was to prepare the body for the pathologist's examination. But it all went well – Adelaide had died from natural causes. She had not consumed any weedkiller and we had no idea why the tin was in her hand as she had died. That was another mystery.

The big mystery, of course, was why she had lived in such poverty while hoarding so much money in her house. There was more than £100,000 and it all went to Salvation Army funds – although they did give £5,000 to our own police widows' pension fund.

I have often pondered Adelaide's fate, wondering why people deny themselves the necessities of life in order to leave enormous wealth which they can never enjoy.

Another common form of miserliness is found in those with money who will spend it on large, expensive items but who will be mean to the extreme when it comes to the smaller essentials.

For example, I knew a man who would willingly spend up to £100 on a pair of shoes, but when the laces broke, he would not buy a new pair. He would tie knots in the broken laces or even made do with old laces from discarded shoes. Thus he walked around in beautiful shoes with tatty, odd-coloured laces.

In one of the moorland farms above Aidensfield was a lady whose actions puzzled me. She was called Betty Barton and I could never make up my mind whether she was mean or just lazy because she rarely emptied the teapot. She employed a massive metal pot, the kind one used to see on railway stations, in transport cafes and during events where lots of people gathered for tea, like agricultural shows or garden parties. It was one of those pots that could fill dozens of cups without being replenished and that's how Betty operated.

Her massive teapot would permanently sit on the hearth, very close to the warmth of the blazing fire even in the height of summer, and whenever she wanted a cup of tea, she simply poured in hot water from the kettle that was always on the hob. The bottom half of the teapot was always full of old tea-leaves and, if the resultant brew was rather weak, she would simply add a spoonful or two of fresh leaves – without emptying the old ones. The thick mass of brown sludge at the bottom simply grew deeper and deeper, but Betty seemed to enjoy the drink that it produced. On one occasion, I was handed a mug of such tea and it was terrible, something akin to that which might have emerged from a witch's cauldron.

Fortunately, as I tasted the first mouthful, she went outside to see why the dog was barking and I managed to pour my mugful into a pot of stew which was bubbling over the fire. I had no idea how long the base contents of her stew had been in her terrible pot, but ever afterwards, whenever I called at her farm, I refused her offers of a cup of tea by saying I'd just had a cup elsewhere. I do not know whether she thought she was saving money or whether tea was supposed to be made in this manner.

Whether Betty was mean is open to argument, but we did get tight-fisted characters within the police force. I knew a superintendent who would never buy a newspaper; he would send the cadet out to the newsagents to fetch a *Northern Echo* and would read it in his office, then send it back to the newsagents with a message saying it was not the edition he wanted. The same fellow once invited a friend and his wife to make up a foursome for a day out in his car; he proposed they toured the countryside in the Yorkshire Dales and so they did, having a most enjoyable time – until the superintendent sent his friend a bill for half the cost of the petrol. And I knew another who calculated the cost of the week's groceries and then gave his wife that precise amount, even down to halfpennies, thus for one week's housekeeping she'd be given £8 15s 2½d and next week, for example, she received £8 12s 6d. The same fellow sold his wife the vegetables which he grew in his own garden – and they were for their own consumption!

A lady of similar mentality was Mrs Angelica Hastings-Waugh, the wife of Lt Col Pemberton Hastings-Waugh (ret.). They lived in a splendid house with splendid gardens and splendid views, and had lots of splendid friends. The splendid Mrs Hastings-Waugh liked to use the word splendid.

She drove around in a splendid old Rover motor-car, visiting friends for coffee or to play bridge, and she was a member of all the important groups in Aidensfield, such as the Parochial Church Council, the Hunt Committee and the splendid Ashfordly Ladies Luncheon Club, of which she had been chairman several times. She was never short of money and accordingly, was never short of splendid friends, so she did enjoy a busy and rather splendid social life. She was often asked to open things too, like garden fêtes, village produce shows, pet shows and a range of similarly splendid events.

There is little doubt that Mrs Hastings-Waugh regarded

herself as a very splendid person, the sort that no self-respecting village should be without, and she always dressed immaculately, even when popping into the shop to buy a jar of jam – the finest and most splendid, of course, the sort one would normally purchase from Harrods. The shop had secured a supply especially for her, such was her splendid taste. And, of course, the lesser ladies bought the same jam, simply because Mrs Hastings-Waugh preferred it. In matters of such grave importance and as an arbiter of good taste, Mrs Hastings-Waugh set the standards which the others tried to emulate.

In the village, we knew this as the Hastings-Waugh Effect, a mental condition which was very like the Alexandra Limp. For those not aware of the latter trend in highly regarded social behaviour, this is the story. In the 1860s, Queen Alexandra, who was then the Princess of Wales, developed a slight limp following a minor accident. In a desire to emulate the Princess, the fashonable ladies of the time all developed a similar slight limp; it was considered very fashionable indeed to limp in an identical manner and so the court ladies, and the fashionable creatures of the time, all began to copy the royal limp. It must have been a strange sight, but this oddity became known as the Alexandra Limp.

In Aidensfield, therefore, the splendid Hastings-Waugh Effect was remarkably similar, being slavishly copied by certain village ladies. The more commercial-minded residents cultivated and nurtured the Effect because, knowing how silly some women can be, they realized they could make money from their behaviour.

For example, the shopkeepers in places like Ashfordly, Eltering and Strensford were all acutely aware of the Hastings-Waugh Effect; they knew that whenever she bought anything, her disciples would do likewise and so the stores ensured they always had sufficient stocks to supply her ardent followers. Everything from shoes to washing-up powder by way of hats, glossy magazines or lampshades, was kept for those splendid ladies who suffered from the Hastings-Waugh Effect.

If Mrs Hastings-Waugh purchased a bottle of Fairy Liquid

instead of some other ordinary washing-up fluid, then twenty other ladies would do likewise; if she bought a Madeira cake instead of a plain fruit cake or jam sponge, then twenty ladies would want Madeira cakes; if she bought a purple dress with white spots on, so would twenty other ladies, even if they never dared to wear their latest fashion in public.

But Mrs Hastings Waugh, sometimes nicknamed Wastings-Hore by the less savoury of local society, had a curious quirk to her own character, one about which few people knew.

She hoarded freebies. If she went into a restaurant, for example, she would fill her handbag with sugar-lumps because they were free. She would stuff cocktail sticks into her handbag along with paper napkins and uneaten nibbles. She would collect bars of soap from hotel bathrooms, sheets of toilet-paper from the loos, and shoe-cleaning tissues from the polishing place in smart hotels. When, in later years, hotels and restaurants adopted the practice of making use of sachets of sauce, mustard, sugar, salt and pepper, she would collect those, filling her handbag with dozens of them, and later she began to add those small thimble-sized cartons of milk or cream that are given away at motorway service areas with coffee or tea. She took books of paper matches and free samples of anything given away at promotional events, such as new soups, perfumes or soft drinks.

She practised this mania for years; from time to time long after I left Aidensfield, I would be attending an event at which she and her husband were present, and I always watched her, waiting the time her hands speedily and surreptitiously whipped the freebie from the table and into her handbag with the speed of light. She was an expert at operating unseen, a truly gifted craftsperson, an agile operator with fingers and hands whose movements were rapid enough to qualify as sleight of hand. She could have become a noted card manipulator and I formed the view that she could have been a very successful magician or pick-pocket. For this reason, I found some strange fascination in watching for the moment she struck; it was rather like a viper striking at its prey or trying to see how a conjurer performs a complicated card trick.

I learned of her passion during an event at Aidensfield. For most ladies, the occurrence would have been a social disaster but it did not appear to embarrass Mrs Hastings-Waugh.

Aidensfield Women's Institute had organized a garden fête which was held in the splendidly spacious grounds of Causey House, the home of the Hastings-Waughs. With splendid and expansive views towards the Roman road and the surrounding moorland, the house was magnificently built of local stone with splendid mullioned windows, and it was more like a manorial hall than a mere country house. Its grounds, well kept by two permanent gardeners, offered a splendid setting for the fête.

And, of course, who should be asked to open it but the splendid Mrs Angelica Hastings-Waugh herself?

Scheduled to begin at 2 p.m., a serious problem arose because Mrs Hastings-Waugh had a long-standing and very important appointment which could not be broken. It was an appointment with her hairdresser; she had arranged to have her hair restyled at Eltering at 2 p.m. that very day, and so, to accommodate her, the WI altered the time of the opening ceremony to 1.30 p.m. As a consequence, Mrs Hastings-Waugh could perform the necessary ritual with a few well-chosen words and still be in time to honour the hairdresser with her presence. I was at the fête too. I was on duty and patrolling the village to prevent cars blocking the roads; I had to ensure there was room for passage of the emergency services should something dramatic occur, something the public often forgets about when parking.

As the excited crowd assembled before the elevated stage to await words of wisdom from their goddess, Mr Hastings-Waugh brought her car to the gate, ready for a flying start upon her very important journey and I stood in front of it to prevent anyone blocking her in. One has to get one's priorities right in such splendid circumstances.

Mrs Hastings-Waugh, superbly adorned in her splendid salmon-pink outfit with a broad-brimmed hat, white blouse, matching shoes and large handbag, was fit to grace a royal occasion and, after giving a simply splendid opening address, swept away towards her car.

Her husband had the engine ticking over, I held the gate

open as she swept onward like a galleon in full sail, but just as she reached the car, a little girl appeared from nowhere to present her with a bouquet of flowers. Mrs Hastings-Waugh had rushed off the podium without giving the child her own moment of glory, but the child had had the wit to chase after her and had caught her prey just as she was leaving. Mrs Hastings-Waugh, touched by the gesture, placed her handbag on the roof of the car to leave both hands free as she accepted the flowers; she kissed the child, thanked her profusely and handed the flowers to her husband, saying, 'These are absolutely splendid, Henry; do make sure they are placed in water immediately,' and then she settled behind the steering-wheel. I waved her out of the drive and on to the road as the faithful gathering of fête attenders formed behind to cheer loudly as they waved her off – but as she drew away, I realized she'd left her handbag on the roof of the car. She accelerated rapidly along the road as I shouted for her to stop, but I was too late.

As she drove away, her handbag fell into the village street and burst open to roll along the road. It was a large bag – and from it cascaded hundreds of free packets of sauce and salt, sugar-lumps, books of paper matches, cocktail sticks and bars of hotel soap . . . in seconds, there was a long and somewhat embarrassing trail of her assorted trophies.

She did stop, however; the shouting of her fans had attracted her attention and she halted the car, climbed out and retrieved her handbag, ignoring the spilt contents. With never a comment nor even a show of embarrassment, she resumed her drive as her followers rushed out to gather up the freebies.

I thought the moment would have embarrassed her, but apparently it did not. Her devoted followers all rushed out to buy equally commodious handbags and they began to emulate her, filling them with all manner of free gifts – taken from absolutely the right places, of course, all very splendid and the perfect place for ladies of quality to frequent. The Hastings-Waugh Effect was very strong in Aidensfield but for the life of me, I do not know what prompts some women to slavishly copy those whom they regard as leaders.

The new mass hobby of collecting freebies must have cost

the local tradesmen, hoteliers and restaurateurs a fortune in handouts although, on reflection, the Hastings-Waugh adherents must have had to spend money in a wide range of very splendid establishments in order to obtain their splendid freebies.

Looking back upon the incident, I reckon that, hidden within the depths of the businessmen's attitude to the Hastings-Waugh Effect, there are distant flashes of rather splendid Yorkshire fiscal wisdom.

Another aspect of meanness manifests itself in certain avid collectors. They will strive to make their collection the finest in the universe even if it is considered trivia by many.

Such is their ardour, that they will never part with any item of their collection, unless it is to replace it with something of greater rarity or interest. Some collections of what seems trivia, however, do become extremely valuable – collectors of comics, magazines, autographs, photographs, toy cars, bottles, inkwells, beer mats, the work of obscure artists, old books, advertisements and other assorted objects and ephemera can provide fine examples of this. But in Aidensfield, we had a lady whose lifelong passion was her collection of photographs which, over the years, became the object of desire by many local residents and others with commercial leanings. She had collected hundreds of photographs of the Elsinby Flood.

The Elsinby Flood occurred in July 1893. On the moors behind the village, there was a cloudburst of unbelievably intense ferocity after which a deluge of water rushed from the heights towards Elsinby in the dale below. Along the route, it gathered more water until it was a roaring torrent which became channelled into a gully, ripping trees from the hillsides, moving boulders and carrying before it struggling livestock such as sheep and cattle which had been too late to avoid it. This huge wall of water, more than seven feet deep, hit the village like a tidal wave.

It demolished several cottages and barns in its path before spreading across the floor of the dale, and soon it was more than five feet deep across almost the entire ground upon which

Elsinby stood. The little valley had become a lake of muddy water. Almost the entire village had been made awash beneath five feet of fluid slime; trees, shrubs, mud, boulders and dead livestock filled the village street and most of the houses had floodwater up to chest height.

This flash flood rivalled the famous floods of Langtoft in the Yorkshire Wolds but the astonishing thing was that no one was killed. A colossal amount of water had accumulated within a matter of minutes but recovery from the devastation took months – it was several days before the water subsided to leave behind a terrible wasteland of thick, stinking mud and debris. Every house in Elsinby suffered the effects; furniture was destroyed, the foundations of houses damaged and farms were ruined. One of the few places left untouched was the village school because it was perched on a piece of rising ground and so it escaped the waters. It became a place of refuge for the children until the flood subsided.

In spite of the trauma, several residents and some incoming sightseers had the foresight to take photographs of the flood, some immediately afterwards and others over the period of drying-out and during the subsequent replenishment of the village and the rehabilitation of its inhabitants.

The pictures, amateurish, faded and brown in many cases, provided a remarkable record of the disaster, but apart from an article in the local gazette and some features in various magazines, none were published.

By and large, the photographs were very personal ones and the village people had kept their own photographs as mementoes; some were in home-made frames on cottage walls while others were stored in old bureaux, wardrobes and cupboards. Over the years, as cottages were sold and the occupants moved away or died, so lots of those old photographs were dispersed or sold in auctions. Many got thrown out or handed to relatives who did not particularly treasure them; many were simply misplaced.

Thanks to the actions of a certain lady, however, many Elsinby photographs did survive. She had the foresight to begin collecting photographs of the flood.

She was Mrs Beatrice Wintergill of Penwick House,

Elsinby, who was born in 1887. She was six when the flood had roared through the village and was one of the children who had witnessed its devastation from the security of the school. She was then called Beatrice Simpson. She had married Arthur Wintergill in 1907 and in 1915, when she was only twenty-eight, Arthur was killed in World War I. The young Mrs Wintergill returned to Elsinby to live with her only child, a son called Thomas who was then five years old. Her husband had left her well provided for and she had no need to earn her own living; money was never a problem.

Arthur Wintergill had come from a professional and very successful family in Bradford with interests in woollen manufacture, and so, in her new widowhood but with some wealth to her name, she had bought Penwick House. This was a large square house which she remembered as being swamped with water during the flood, and it still stands today, having never since suffered a similar fate.

Upon her return to live in Elsinby, Beatrice joined in the village life, becoming a parish councillor, a school governor and member of the parochial church council. In addition, she had started to research the flood disaster with the intention of writing an account of it for a local periodical and had to assemble some photographs.

By 1917, when she was thirty, Beatrice had become an ardent collector of flood photographs, now realizing that if she did not save them, many would be thrown out, lost or destroyed. I did learn that some unknown force compelled her to add to her collection; she seemed to be seeking an elusive picture, but the outcome was that by 1947, she had a most impressive collection, all catalogued and framed. Many of her photographs adorned the walls of her lovely home. She was then sixty but far from retired; her son had gone to Australia to run a sheep farm and she continued to haunt auction rooms, house sales, second-hand shops and other likely places in York, Harrogate, Hull and elsewhere, often locating just one more faded snapshot or photograph of the flood. She never stopped hunting them.

A comprehensive collection of photographs of the flood had become her life's work; it had become an obsession in fact, for she scoured the entire country for pictures, having found one in a Brighton antique shop, another in a picture gallery in Birmingham and another in Keswick, tucked into the pages of a guide-book. When I became the village constable at Aidensfield, therefore, Beatrice was approaching her eighties and still hunting Elsinby Flood photographs. In 1967, she reached the age of 80 but was still a sprightly, remarkably fit and very intelligent lady.

The residents of Elsinby, in recognition of her years of work for the community, decided to honour her with a party in the village hall. The postman, Gilbert Kingston, suggested that the hall also be host to an exhibition of her photographic collection. Hitherto, she had never permitted a public exhibition of her photographs, although she did show them to visitors to her home. They could look, but not touch. She had become a jealous guardian of the collection and had a deep-seated fear that future generations might not care for it in the way that she had. But Gilbert was a persuasive character and even though she said her collection was incomplete, he managed to convince her that the villagers had a right to view these remarkable pictures. And so in July 1967, seventy-four years after the disaster, Elsinby Village Hall Committee staged a party for Beatrice which coincided with an exhibition of her huge collection.

The walls and many display stands showed the pictures to good advantage and in fact, two more pictures were presented to her at her birthday party, having been found by an old lady still living in the village. Afterwards, the exhibition remained on display for a month, with coffee and refreshments being sold and the public being charged an entrance fee to view it.

I popped in from time to time, both to inspect the pictures and to show my uniform as a means of giving some protection with the occasional piece of advice about their security, but Gilbert had done a good job. None of the photos had been harmed in any way.

On the day before the exhibition was due to close, I popped in and found he was alone. He offered me a coffee which I accepted.

'It's been a good exhibition, Nick, we've created immense

interest about the village history, with the school kids doing a project. At the time, the school kids had a grandstand view of the flood, and besides, lots of visitors and locals want to know more. Beatrice's collection has worked magic for us, the hall's benefited too, the extra income's very useful.'

'So what happens to the photographs next?'

'They will be returned to Beatrice.'

'But she's not getting any younger,' I commented, echoing the thoughts of many. 'It's a pity these couldn't become a permanent exhibition, either here or somewhere else.'

'She's frightened of losing them, she's spent a lifetime gathering them and always maintains the collection is not complete. Just when we think there's no more photographs left anywhere on this globe, someone finds another and gives it to her. She's terrified that just one gets lost or damaged. She has insisted she gets them back and she agreed to us having them until tomorrow. I had a devil of a job persuading her to release them at all for this exhibition so I don't want to squeeze any more concessions out of her. The fact that she got another two photos for her collection has helped her to come to terms with this public viewing, so the chance of others being discovered might influence her to allow more exhibitions.'

'So what's their long-term future?' I pressed him.

'When she dies, they go to her son. He's in Australia, but I understand he's thinking of returning to England to retire. He'll be well on his way to sixty now and must soon be thinking of retirement.'

'So what'll he do with them?'

'Dunno, unless Beatrice imposes a condition or makes some stipulation in her will.'

'It would be a crying shame if they got lost or dispersed after all her efforts.' I sipped the coffee. 'I just hope her son knows what to do with them. They could become a permanent exhibition here, or at one of the local museums or libraries.'

'That's what we told Beatrice; we asked if she would leave them to the village, or even to a local museum, but she is determined to leave them to Thomas. She's made that abundantly clear, Nick, she seems to think that a family interest will safeguard the collection, but lots of people have been pestering her about their future. One antique dealer made a huge offer for the lot, well over a thousand pounds, but she refused. We had others in too, all making noises about buying the collection; a photographer came and he offered to reproduce them for sale, giving her a royalty on every one he sold – she refused him, too. Mind, it shows that some folks realize how valuable the whole collection is. It's unique, in fact.'

'And don't forget it's her lifetime's work,' I added.

I left Gilbert when a car-load of visitors arrived, taking a last lingering look at the photographs as I walked out.

Two days later when I popped into the hall, it was deserted as it awaited the annual Elsinby Show of Vegetable Produce and Crafts. Beatrice had got her precious photographs back and her collection was still intact.

It would be several months later when sad news reached Elsinby. Beatrice's son, Thomas, had died suddenly in Australia and before his death, he had expressed a wish to be buried in Elsinby. His death and eventual funeral in the village resurrected all the interest in Beatrice's collection of photographs because, if her son and heir was dead and gone, who would now inherit her collection?

It bothered Gilbert Kingston who tried to talk to her about it once her period of mourning was over, but it also energized a host of antique dealers, photographers, journalists, writers and other collectors, all of whom began to visit the village in the hope of persuading Beatrice to part with her collection. But she steadfastly refused and gave no indication of her wishes for the eventual disposal of the photographs.

Before I left Aidensfield, Beatrice went into a decline and was taken to a private nursing home in York. A friend from Elsinby looked after the house and made sure that her precious collection of photographs was not harmed or removed, but within six months, Beatrice had died. None of us knew the fate of the photographs, but when her will was published, we learned she had done the right thing.

She had left them to the village school, asking that they form a permanent exhibition upon its walls in memory of her own recollection of the flood from that very place. She did add a proviso that a body of three trustees be formed to care for the collection in perpetuity and that they be given the authority to arrange external exhibitions in the village hall, or in such other place as they deemed suitable, any proceeds being shared between the village hall and the trustees, the trustees to use their share for maintenance of the collection. Reproductions could be permitted and any royalties accruing should be paid for the benefit of the school.

She wanted any income to be utilized to buy books and other educational aids. The collection was to be known as The Beatrice Wintergill Collection.

It is still providing much-needed funds for Elsinby Primary School and a further seven photographs have been added since her death. The last one to be received shows Beatrice as a 6-year-old girl; she is standing outside the school gazing at the floodwaters as they swirl around the village.

This was the one picture she never found; I think this was the missing one, the one which drove her to hunt for every possible photograph. But not a single other photograph has been discovered since that time.

With the picture of Beatrice, aged six, gazing upon the floodwaters from the school, the Beatrice Wintergill Collection is now complete. She would be pleased about that.

6 Men of Dubious Ability

'Tis God gives skill,
But not without men's hands:
He could not make Antonio Stradivari's
    violins
Without Antonio.

Mary Ann Evans (George Eliot) 1819–80

One fine spring morning as I was walking down the village
street in Aidensfield in full uniform, I heard a strange sound.
It was rather like a stone hitting metal, something akin to a
pebble being propelled with great force at a tin can or even
thrown up by the tyre of a passing car to strike a roadside
direction sign.

Puzzled, I looked around and almost immediately noticed
that the weather-vane on the tower of the parish church was
spinning wildly. Something had struck it with considerable
force and I wondered if it was one of the village youths testing
his skills with an air rifle – the vane, in the shape of a cockerel,
was far too high and far too remote from the road to have been
hit by a pebble thrown up by a passing car. I saw no one and
heard nothing further; the weather-vane was still intact and
from my vantage point did not appear to have suffered any
damage, so I resumed my patrolling.

Although puzzled by this, I did not consider it worthy of
further investigation until a couple of days later.

A similar incident happened when I was talking to George
Ward outside his pub. Before our very eyes, a starling
suddenly toppled from its perch on the rim of a chimney-pot
just along the street.

'Somebody's shot it!' cried George as the stricken bird

landed on the pavement with a thud.

'I didn't hear any shots,' I commented as I went forward for a closer look. The bird was dead and a trickle of blood oozed from its nostrils and beak, but there was no outward sign of injury. It hadn't been shot. There was no indication that it had been struck by either air-gun pellets, shotgun pellets or a rifle bullet; it looked as if it had been stunned.

'That's bloody funny,' said George, and I then told him about the weather-vane. Standing where I was, it was easy to see that if someone had been responsible for both actions, the missiles had come from roughly the same area. I popped the dead starling into a waste-bin and went on my way.

In the days that followed, I heard of several similar incidents, all minor in their own way while collectively they presented a puzzle. It was not something with which to exercise my official mind, however. None the less, I was curious about other reports. People in the village had seen a beer bottle, left on a wall by a drinker, suddenly shatter for no apparent reason. Old Mr Harker had his trilby hat knocked off by an unknown force and a garden gnome had his nose removed.

A pair of Miss Fogarty's red silk knickers had suddenly soared from her washing-line when there was not a breath of wind and a tom cat, wooing his heart's desire from an outhouse roof, suddenly fled with a piercing yowl. A ripe tomato was reported to have splattered against the window of a woman who persistently complained about rubbish littering the Greengrass ranch while one notoriously bad local driver ran into a rotten egg which sailed on to his car from behind a hedge. It splattered across his windscreen to make a ghastly mess.

It was around that time that I realized Claude Jeremiah Greengrass had a house guest. That is a polite way of saying someone was dossing down with him and, at that time, I did not link that character with the mysterious events of the village. On occasions, I saw them together in the pub and once or twice spotted them striding across the moors outside the village, or roaming the fields nearer to habitation with the faithful lurcher, Alfred, in attendance. Claude's companion was smaller than his host, but equally scruffy and readily identifiable by a mop of thick ginger hair, rather like the well-used spikes of a wire brush. He would be in his mid-forties and had a round, impish face with several days' growth of gingerish-grey beard. He had arrived in an old van and had all the appearance of an itinerant scrap-dealer.

'Who's the fellow with Claude Jeremiah?' I asked George in the pub one morning.

'It's his cousin,' George told me. 'He comes to stay with Claude Jeremiah from time to time.'

'Not another Greengrass!' I cried.

'There's quite a clan of them scattered about the moors,' he laughed. 'This is just one of them, he's called Zachariah Solomon Knapweed. You've not met him?'

'Never,' I said. 'Is that his real name?'

'The family was a great one for finding unusual names, Nick. How about Anastasia Fabiola Greengrass – that was Claude's mother and there was his aunt, Anastasia's sister, who was Matilda Dymphna Knapweed – she was Zachariah Solomon's mum.'

'What's he do, this cousin?' I asked.

·'Not a lot, scrap-dealing generally, a bit of potato picking or hay-timing, general labouring.'

'General lay-abouting you mean!' I'd met characters like this on previous occasions. 'So what's he doing here?'

'If I know the pair of them, it'll be a spot of poaching supplemented by a bit of wheeler-dealing in dodgy goods, Nick.'

'I'll keep my eye on the pair of them,' I assured him.

The first intimation that there was any link between the arrival of Zachariah Solomon and the mysterious shootings was when Ted Barnes, one of Lord Ashfordly's gamekeepers, called at the office of my hilltop police house in Aidensfield. He was carrying a brace of dead pheasants.

'We've had a bashing, Nick.' He dumped the dead birds on the floor. 'Last night. Umpteen pheasants have been taken with never a sound. My dogs would have barked if there'd been guns but they left those two behind, missed 'em in the pick-up.'

'Shot, are they?' I asked.

'No, that's why I brought 'em along. There's no shot in 'em, Nick, no pellet from an air-gun nor lead from a shotgun. They've not been netted either, nor given boozy raisins to make 'em dizzy enough to fall off their perches. No, Nick, they were stunned, look. Knocked cold while roosting up aloft.'

He pointed to the head of each bird and I noticed the trickle of blood from their nostrils and beaks. I touched their heads and found that one of the skulls was definitely smashed.

'You can keep these, with Lord Ashfordly's compliments,' said Ted.

'Thanks, they'll make a nice meal. You know, Ted, I saw a starling like this the other day,' and I told him about the other occurrences that had happened locally.

'If it wasn't for that peculiar cause of death, I'd swear it was Claude Jeremiah,' said Ted. 'But this is more like a catapult wound. He never uses a catapult.'

'He's got a cousin staying with him right now,' I commented.

'Cousin? Not Zachariah Solomon?' There was a shocked tone in Ted's voice. 'One of those bloody Knapweeds?'

'The very same, Ted. You know him?'

'There's your villain, Nick. Zachariah Solomon Knapweed, the finest shot anywhere with a catapult. He can hit a flying sparrow with one of his clay marbles.'

I was then treated to an account of the dubious skills of Claude Jeremiah's cousin; whatever an expert could achieve with a firearm, Zachariah Solomon could match with his catapult. He used small clay marbles as his ammunition. They were rounded and precise in size and shape, and thus far more accurate and reliable than mere misshapen pebbles. We called them clayies for they were made from clay and had the fragile texture of something like a clay plant-pot. Glass marbles would have been just as effective, but they were far more expensive – and clayies often shattered into tiny fragments on impact, thus destroying themselves whilst virtually removing any evidence of their use.

With his clayies, Zachariah Solomon could hit a halfpenny

thrown into the air; he could knock the drawer out of a matchbox held endwise in someone's hand, pushing it from its casing, yet leaving the casing intact; he could fire into the opening of a jam jar laid on its side at fifty yards and make his clayie come to rest without smashing the glass. He could hit birds in flight and was extremely accurate even at long distance. Ted told me he'd even competed in a clay-pigeon contest and had beaten many of the guns with his catapult. The fellow was a catapult wizard.

I knew that this was the character who could send weather-vanes whirring, knickers flying and sleeping pheasants to their sudden death.

After listening to Ted's account, which contained a good deal of grudging admiration for Zachariah Solomon's skills, I decided to pay a visit to the Greengrass establishment. When I arrived, the cousins were changing the spark-plugs on Zachariah's old van, apparently because it was spluttering a lot.

'Now then, Claude,' I greeted him as I tried to avoid the mud and sludge which adorned his approach road.

'Hello, Mr Rhea.' He looked up from the dirty engine. 'Just doing some repairs, she's missing when she's pulling, it's a duff plug if you ask me.'

'I was just passing and thought I'd pop in,' I said, walking around the old vehicle. Pieces of its bodywork hung off and there were holes where it had lost the battle against rust and rot. And it was not taxed.

'I haven't done owt, Mr Rhea.' He jerked his head. 'Not me, I'm behaving these days.'

'You've got a cousin staying, I'm told,' I smiled at him as he emerged from beneath the bonnet, rubbing his hands with an oily rag. 'Zachariah Solomon.'

'Aye, he's stopping over for a few days, we get on well.'

'I hear he's a dab hand with a catapult,' I said.

'Oh aye, he can hit a sparrow in flight at fifty yards, Mr Rhea – not that he would, mind, sparrows being nice chirpy little things.'

'And I bet he could send a weather-vane whirring, or knock hats off old gentlemen . . . .'

'You'd better ask him to show you, Mr Rhea,' said Claude, who then put his fingers to his mouth and whistled through them. At the sound, Alfred the lurcher appeared with a puzzled frown on his narrow face, but likewise a ginger-headed fellow poked his head around a barn door and shouted, 'Is it 'lowance time?'

'Aye, if you make t'tea,' laughed Claude.

Zachariah did make the tea and emerged with a plate of cakes and three mugs on a tray; I felt quite surprised to find he had arranged 'lowance for a constable and waited with considerable interest as Zachariah placed the plate of cakes and the mugs on top of an old oil drum.

'This is Mr Rhea, our local constable,' Claude Jeremiah made the introductions. 'He's been hearing about you.'

'Now then, Zachariah,' I nodded a greeting as I accepted a chipped and stained mug full of tea, risking a sip before making any further move. It was quite tasty and refreshing, to be honest.

'What's he been hearing?' Zachariah asked as he lifted his mug from the oil drum. I was not sure whether to help myself to one of the scones just yet, or wait to be offered one.

I decided to wait for the plate to be handed around.

'He's heard about you and your catapult,' Claude told his cousin before we had our scones. 'Show the constable what you can do, Zachariah.'

Unable to resist the challenge, Zachariah placed an egg in an eggcup and asked me to hold it high at arm's length. With some reservation I did so and Zachariah then walked away, about the length of a cricket pitch, then pulled an enormous wooden catapult from his inside pocket. With the speed of light, he took aim and shot at the egg; the top was sliced off as cleanly as if I'd done it with a spoon. He followed with a bewildering demonstration of accuracy and speed. He hit coins thrown in the air, sent tins flying from a wall, each being struck before its predecessor hit the ground and then he fired one shot high into the air, waiting for it to return and it did – straight down a fallpipe at the end of the house. It was an astonishing display, and all done with tiny clayies. I applauded Zachariah and congratulated him, asking if he'd ever thought of giving exhibitions of his skills, but he shook his head. 'I don't like crowds,' was all he said.

But while we had been watching Zachariah, two of the three scones had vanished.

'That bloody Alfred!' cursed Claude Jeremiah. 'That dog has no manners, eating guests' food . . . Alfred!' and he went off to remonstrate with the thieving dog which had had the sense to hide itself.

One scone remained on the oil drum, but even as Claude vanished, an amazing thing happened. A cheeky and very determined grey squirrel had sneaked from the surrounding trees. It had apparently seen the scone, for it leapt on to the drum and picked up the delicacy in its forelegs, using its tiny hands to grip the food. And then, with the utmost cheek, it began to eat it. Had it also taken the others? I wondered if Alfred was being falsely accused of a crime, then Zachariah acted like lightning. In a split second, he whirled around with his catapult, loosed a clayie at the squirrel and hit it somewhere in its midrib area. The animal screeched in agony, dropped the scone and scuttled away.

Zachariah laughed. 'Bloody thing,' he said. 'It got my boiled egg yesterday, little varmints they are.'

I knew that grey squirrels were considerably adept at stealing, being one of our more persistent pests, but I noted that Zachariah did not kill it. He had aimed to bruise, not to kill.

'You didn't kill him?' I said.

'Nay, Constable, I like the little sods! Just taught him a lesson, bruised his ribs, but he'll be back. He nicked a bit of my roast beef from my Sunday dinner last time I was here . . . .'

He launched into a hilarious account of coping with thieving squirrels at the Greengrass abode, but I had my duty to do.

'Claude,' I said when he returned without finding Alfred, 'I think Alfred's innocent, just ask Zachariah.'

'I'm not so sure, Mr Rhea, I know Alfred, you see . . . .'

'Well, anyway, thanks for the tea, very nice – and thanks to Zachariah for making it. But I'm here on duty . . . .'

'I didn't think it was a social call, Mr Rhea, not that you're not welcome here any time, of course, but . . . .'

'Ted Barnes called this morning,' I told the cousins. 'Lord

Ashfordly's gamekeeper. He said somebody had given his pheasants a bashing last night.'

'I've no idea who that could be, Mr Rhea,' said Claude.

'A catapult was used to kill the birds as they roosted in the trees,' I said. 'No shots were fired from guns, no other devices used. Just the silence of a catapult, Zachariah. The skill of a top-rate catapult expert, it was the epitome of marksmanship combined with the stealth of a natural poacher . . . .' I watched their faces as I rambled on.

Zachariah looked at Claude and Claude looked at Zachariah.

'We'd never do anything like that, Mr Rhea,' they chorused in unison.

'If I decide to examine each of your vans for feathers or blood, do you reckon I'll find any?' I asked, looking across the yard towards the two battered vehicles.

They said nothing, so I continued, 'Or if I search the house, might I find a plucked pheasant or two, or some nice specimens hanging for later consumption?'

'One pheasant is just like any other pheasant, Mr Rhea.' Claude Jeremiah spoke with confidence, knowing how difficult it was to identify such creatures to the satisfaction of a court.

He was saying that if there was pheasant in the house, no one could prove it was precisely the one which had come from Lord Ashfordly's estate.

'In this case you're wrong, Claude,' I told him. 'Because if you have any pheasants which were killed last night, they'll all have broken skulls, injuries caused by a catapulted clay marble and not a gun of any sort. So they will be identifiable, you see, no other pheasants will have those injuries, Claude . . . .'

'Aye, well, there's none like that here, Mr Rhea, honest, you can look.'

'Thanks, I will,' and I did, but found nothing. They had clearly sold their ill-gotten gains very quickly and thus there was no evidence of their activities. I could not proceed with a charge of poaching.

'Now,' I said, turning to Zachariah. 'Your van. It's not

taxed, I see . . . .'

'It's not on the road, Constable,' beamed Zachariah Solomon. 'It doesn't need to be taxed when it's not on the road . . . .'

'But it will have to go on to the road to leave here,' I said. 'And I'll be waiting, then I can check its insurance and your driving licence, and test it for faults in its brakes, lights, steering. In fact, in its present condition, with all that rust, it looks as if it might have dangerous parts and accessories too . . . .'

I turned to leave and as a parting shot, said, 'Claude, I'm going to visit the hotels and cafés in the area, just to see if they've bought any pheasants from you lately, pheasants with broken skulls and free from gunshot. If they have, I'll know where they came from, won't I?'

The veiled threat was enough. Early next morning, Zachariah Solomon Knapweed left his cousin's house and I did not catch him driving his old van because I was on late duty. But there was no more catapult vandalism in and around Aidensfield, not did Ashfordly estate lose any more pheasants to the doubtful skills of Claude Jeremiah's catapult-wielding cousin.

But the family's legacy lived on – I think it was probably Alfred who baffled the vicar during a garden party. The reverend gentleman had obtained a plate of sandwiches and buns but had been interrupted before he could devour them. Being a good-mannered cove, he held the plate low and to one side while engaged in a riveting conversation with a lady parishioner about family bias in the cleaning rota. By the time she'd gone, so had his sandwiches and buns.

They had simply vanished from the plate and had not been spilled on to the ground; there is every reason to suspect it was the action of Alfred who was seen, at the material time, licking his lips and wagging his tail at the unsuspecting vicar.

But proof of his guilt would be difficult to obtain. Greengrass had trained the dog well.

One of the major events in Aidensfield was the annual show. It was held in a field behind the church and consisted of livestock displays, pony classes, competitions involving flowers, fruit, vegetables, home-made produce, knitting and assorted crafts, showjumping demonstrations, music from the Aidensfield and District String Orchestra, sports for the children with tests of strength for the menfolk such as tossing the sheaf or racing with a sack of potatoes upon their shoulders. In addition, there was a whole panoply of associated events and the gathering was held on the last Saturday of August.

In general, the morning session, which began at 10 a.m. was utilized for the judging of all competition entries and while this was being done, there were livestock classes, jumping and pony events. Members of the public were permitted entry from noon and, as usual, a large crowd was expected.

For several years, the opening ceremony had been a rather unusual one. It consisted of a remarkable demonstration of sheep-shearing by the renowned Hodgson brothers. Each was a sheep-shearing champion in his own right and they had the memorable names of Matthew, Mark, Luke and John. Their father had been Peter Hodgson, himself a noted sheep farmer from the moors, and he had trained and encouraged his sons to emulate and improve upon his own skills. It was the boast of each man that he could completely shear one sheep by hand in the time it took for Aidensfield parish church clock to strike twelve. It was a demonstration of speed and skill which was hard to beat and exciting to watch.

To illustrate the speed of this achievement, a world record for hand-shearing sheep was set by a New Zealander in 1976, when, using a solo blade, he hand-sheared 353 lambs in nine hours which is just over thirty-nine animals every hour, or one sheep at roughly every minute and a half. That is a magnificent example of speed, skill and, above all, stamina. I never used a stop-watch to calculate how long it took Aidensfield church clock to strike twelve but I reckon it was around one minute.

On the occasion of show day, therefore, I was on duty at the entrance to the showfield, making sure the gathering traffic did not obstruct the village street, when I learned that

Matthew, Mark, Luke and John were about to perform the opening ceremony.

Traffic was light and I decided to abandon my post to watch them. Everyone wanted to watch because, sooner or later, one of the brothers would fail this very public test; their ages ranged from forty-two (Matthew), forty (Mark), thirty-eight (Luke) to thirty-five (John), and it was felt that age would soon slow them down, especially Matthew. The entire village wondered when one or other would fail to shear his animal in the allotted time. In some ways, it was like watching a motor race in the hope one of the cars would crash . . . .

The brothers were arranged on an elevated platform, each with a sheep held ready for shearing as everyone awaited the first strike of the clock. Each man had his shearer plugged in and switched on, the blades purring like the shears in a gents' hairdressers. As the tension mounted, I found myself standing next to Jonathan Newbould, a new member of the show committee. I would hear from him afterwards, but meanwhile people were looking at their watches and checking them against the large clock which overlooked the ground. The pointers inched their way towards noon and then we heard the first strike. Instantly the brothers set to work cheered on by the crowd and, once again, as the final stroke sounded there were four expertly and cleanly sheared ewes. Everyone applauded and the show was formally declared open by the President.

But it was Jonathan Newbould who said to me, 'I could make those men an automatic set of shears; with them, one man could then shear all four sheep at the same time.'

'Really?' I said.

'I'm an inventor you know, just moved to the village, Newbould's the name, Jonathan.'

'PC Rhea.' I introduced myself and shook his hand. 'The village constable. So what do you invent?'

'Anything,' he said. 'Machinery, kitchen utensils, tools, labour-saving gadgets, gardening equipment . . . .'

'Is there a living in that?' I asked, turning to face my new contact. He was a mild-looking, rather slightly-built man in rather formal clothes, a dark suit, white shirt and dark tie, and would be in his mid-forties. Balding with dark hair above his ears and around his neck, he wore round spectacles and had a small, trim moustache.

'Not at the moment,' he said. 'I work for the district council, in the accounts department, but I invent things in my spare time. I'm hoping, of course, for the big one, something I can patent and which will then earn me a fortune and make me secure for life. I almost did it with a self-clean windscreen wiper . . . .'

'What happened to it?' I asked out of curiosity.

'It was too heavy for the wiper arms of most cars and kept falling off. I'm working on a lighter version now and some of the car manufacturers have expressed an interest. The snag is that the self-cleaning mechanism is so heavy, you see . . . .'

'Doesn't the action of rainwater clean them anyway?' I asked him.

'Well, yes, up to a point, but I'm sure that standards could be improved. I'd like one that would clean greasy screens, you see, and remove dead flies in summer . . . that's my aim, Mr Rhea. What a boon to motorists!'

'And the idea you've just come up with, the mechanized multi-sheep-shearer. That won't be easy to construct, surely, because all sheep are different shapes, if only slightly so?'

'Challenges are there to be overcome, Mr Rhea. I'm sure it will work, and if it does, it might sell in Australia and New Zealand, and other sheep rearing countries, Mr Rhea. You must look beyond the shores of our island, you know, when aiming for the top. Yes, I must work on that idea.' And off he went.

I was to discover that Jonathan Newbould lived in a neat semi-detached house overlooking Aidensfield village green and he had a shed at the bottom of the garden. There, each night, he worked on his inventions and tested them on his friends or wife, sometimes even creating interest in mass manufacturers. I was also to learn, however, that none of them worked. Jonathan invented the kind of thing that one sees advertised in cheap magazines and some Sunday papers, as well as free catalogues. They are gadgets which promise to make life easier and which gullible folks buy, only to find that there is nowhere to store the thing when it is not being used, or that it is simpler to continue in older, well-tested routines.

In spite of his long record of making utterly useless things, his wife thought he was a genius. Daisy Newbould firmly believed in his ideas and provided every possible support for Jonathan and his inventions; she knew that, one day, he would break into the big time and would become a renowned inventor, a household name like Hoover or Biro.

But I had my doubts. One of his ideas was a mechanical scraper for new potatoes. You placed the potato inside, pressed a button and an electric motor set in motion some whirling wire brushes which, so Jonathan believed, would speedily and effectively remove the light skin from any size of new potato. It did – but it also removed most of the flesh too, so you ended with a potato the size of a pea. Also, it would only clean one at a time, so it would take ages to clean a panful.

Fluorescent bedroom slippers were another idea, so you could find them in the dark, but people complained that the light perpetually emitted from the slippers kept them awake. He applied the same logic to a chamberpot, for lots of older country folk still kept a pot under the bed for night-time use. But his idea did not catch on – the potential users had no desire to pee into something that shone up at them from the darkness like a large green eye. Another Jonathan gem was a spirit level which clipped to the shaft of a golf club to inform the player of the gradient of a slope. Several tests showed that it adversely affected one's swing and besides, it was difficult to read while preparing a shot.

Jonathan produced a toothbrush that would clean the top and lower sets of teeth back and front simultaneously, an idea he reckoned would speed up teeth cleaning, and he made a stomach muscle toner too. This was a round clock-shaped device aimed at people who had no time to exercise. It was fitted with an internal large spring which operated a rubber buffer. When wound up like a clock, it had to be strapped to the stomach and when the catch was released, the buffer pummelled the stomach muscles. The idea was that it toned up soft and flabby bellies, but it only served to produce lots of bruises and stomach-ache. Similar contraptions to pound one's arms, legs, thighs and buttocks produced yet more bruises.

He made toe-nail-cutting scissors for left-handed people, a portable deckchair for hikers, a perforated tablespoon which would lift peas from the pan and drain them at the same time, a chopper which would cut and dice carrots in one movement and a cutting device for clipping to a violin bow so that broken strands could be quickly removed by the player.

He made a tray for carrying pot-plants in cars, a spring-handled wash-leather for cleaning high windows, a device to aid one-handed people to wring out dishcloths and face flannels, a circular polisher for cleaning the insides of teapots, a folding walking-stick with umbrella combined, a crumb catcher for people who ate biscuits in bed and an outdoor doormat which switched on a light whenever anyone trod on it.

He produced fitments to fasten to vacuum cleaners so they would clean drains, remove dog hairs from carpets and blow-dry ladies' hairstyles, and a cutting tool for men aged thirty-six and over to clear hairs from their noses and ears.

He made the world's biggest fountain-pen which could write in red, blue, black, green and purple ink, the world's smallest umbrella, a hammock for cats and an expanding ring for holding open paper bags. Spring-loaded clothes-lines, battery-operated salt and pepper shakers and a smoke-free ash-tray were among his inventions. Overboots for keeping wellingtons clean, a pedometer for housewives and musical cricket stumps were projects currently in action as was a self-watering hanging basket. I liked his toilet-paper sheet counter, a device which had to be fixed to a toilet-roll with the counting mechanism being set to monitor the use of every sheet. It told you when the roll was about to run out, something most of us can do with our eyes, and he suggested to me that my police whistle might include an automatic dog whistle so that each time I blew for assistance, I'd be surrounded by a lot of dogs which would warn off any villains who might attack me.

For years after I left Aidensfield, I scrutinized the Sunday papers, magazines and catalogues of innovations, wondering which of the bizarre range of 'useful' gadgets had been invented by Jonathan. So far as I know, he never did invent anything which was genuinely useful, nor, to my knowledge, did he ever complete his multi-sheep-shearer.

In spite of his failure, I did contribute to one of his prototype inventions and my part in his career came when he asked if he could borrow my old police bicycle.

'What do you want it for?' was my first question.

'I've invented an automatic gear-changing mechanism for pedal cycles,' he said with pride. 'It means there will be no more gear changing by hand – as you climb an incline, so the gears will change automatically to suit the gradient. And when you cruise or go down a hill, it will select the correct gear, automatically. Just like the automatic gear-box on expensive cars.'

'It sounds fascinating,' I said. 'But why do you want to use my old bike?'

'Prestige,' he beamed. 'If I fit my gear to your bike and give demonstrations to people like Raleigh or Hercules, they might be willing to build the system into special cycles for police officers. That will be a good advertisement for my idea – you know how people buy the same cars that the police use, well, that logic would apply to my automatic cycle gear.'

'But the police have stopped using pedal cycles,' I told him. 'We're motorized now.'

'Some officers still use them to travel to work.' He was undaunted. 'And I thought, as you don't often use your official cycle now, I might be allowed to fit it with my gear system. I'd test it on your bike. I haven't a bike of my own, you see, and Daisy is sure this will be a world-beater.'

And so I agreed. After all, I hadn't ridden the old black upright for some time and felt it was time to put it to some good use. I let Jonathan take it away and settled back to await being the owner of the world's first fully automatic gear-changing pedal cycle.

In the weeks that followed, Jonathan kept me informed of his progress, inviting me into his shed to examine highly confusing plans which included exploded diagrams containing gear wheels, cogs, ratchets and wires, along with mathematical calculations about stress, gradients and gear ratios. He tried to explain the theory to my numbed mind and I simply nodded and accepted what he told me. I gained the impression that the system would entail something like a conventional three-speed gear of the kind fitted into the hubs of cycle rear wheels, with an added mechanism established in the bottom bracket of the frame, where the pedal spindle passes between each crank. The pressure upon the pedals and thence upon the chain and rear-wheel sprocket would determine the gear to be automatically selected; the steeper the hill, the higher the pressure upon the pedals and thus the lower the gear that would be selected. If this theory worked, the gears would automatically change to suit the climb. Certainly, the theory seemed to point to a feasible invention.

The first breakthrough in his quest for acceptance came with a letter from Raleigh, the cycle manufacturers in Nottingham.

Jonathan had sent them detailed plans of his gears and the experts' response was that, in theory, his system was feasible. If looked as if Jonathan had produced a winner and Raleigh asked him to construct and test a prototype; if that was successful they would examine it with a view to production. Matters like patents and royalties would be discussed if the new gear system was functional. Jonathan was delighted, Daisy was ecstatic and my old bike was to be the test machine.

For several months afterwards, Jonathan would explain that it wasn't quite working properly just yet; things kept jamming, the gear refused to change when necessary, the internal springs did not disengage bottom gear when he reached a flat or downhill run, the pedals sometimes whizzed around without engaging anything but all these problems were, said Jonathan, minor difficulties along the route to building a world-beater.

Eventually, he asked me to witness his first test run. There would be no one else to share in his triumph, apart from the loving and supportive Daisy. Jonathan had selected a short route on the outskirts of Aidensfield. One of the routes in from the moors is via an area known as Ewe Wath, ewe referring to the moorland sheep and wath being a word meaning a ford or foot crossing-place over a beck or stream. Here, years ago, sheep descended from the moors and waded the beck to gain access to the grassy village green in Aidensfield.

Their arrival from the moors was a sign of impending bad weather, but now there is a narrow bridge which accommodates all traffic. The approach to the village comprises a narrow, steeply dropping lane which levels out to cross the stream via that narrow bridge, and after a short flat run, the road twists and then rises gently to cross the railway, followed by a steep climb into the village. George Ward's pub stands at the left of the hilltop, like a sentinel.

From a vantage point on the moorward side of Ewe Wath, it is possible to view the entire route, which is less than a mile, and so it was that on a brisk spring morning, Daisy and I stood at that place to witness Jonathan's journey into the annals of the greats in the history of the pedal cycle. She was armed with a camera and I was simply there to observe. It was my day off, so I was in civilian clothes.

He climbed aboard my old bike and I must say it did not look much different from normal, although he did say he had removed the internal workings of the rear wheel hub to accommodate his own invention. The bottom bracket had changed too, appearing to be more bulky, but the bike itself was my old faithful friend. As he busied himself with the final preparations such as checking the brakes, spinning each pedal, testing the tyres for pressure and so forth, we heard the hoot of an approaching train. 'It's shouting that this is a momentous day in the history of transport,' laughed Jonathan.

'And in our lives, darling,' beamed the proud Daisy.

'I'm ready,' he said, taking a deep breath. I shook his hand and Daisy took his picture astride the machine. And as the oncoming train pulled out of Aidensfield station on its journey across the moors, Jonathan pushed off, raised his left leg to the pedal and began to propel the bike towards the first downward incline – it was the steep drop towards the bridge across the beck.

'It's working, she's moved into top!' he yelled as he sailed down the slope. 'Smooth as satin . . . .'

He was travelling at a very fast speed indeed but his legs were moving slowly, as if he was in a gigantic top gear, and in this manner, he hurtled across the narrow bridge and began the short climb to the railway bridge. He must have been travelling at sixty miles an hour but the true testing time was to come – the bike must now change gear automatically to cope with the steep climb at the other side, a leg-aching ascent which led into the village. I watched, willing him to succeed and then something unexpected and terrible happened.

Something seized up. There was a shout, the bike was brought to a sudden and slithering halt and Jonathan was catapulted from it into the middle of the road. The bike flew across the narrow verge and hit the low parapet of the bridge, then toppled over it – right into the path of the oncoming train. It hooted, there was a screech of iron wheels on metal rails and the entire train shuddered to a halt, but not before it had run over and destroyed my bike.

Daisy was in tears as she ran to the aid of her husband as he struggled to his feet and I went to have words with the engine-driver.

'What bloody fool threw that bike on to the line?' he yelled from his cab. 'It could have gone through a carriage window and killed somebody . . . .'

'An accident,' I shouted back as passengers lowered their windows to watch the drama. 'But he's OK, no bones broken.'

'There'll be hell on if my train's damaged,' he said, climbing on to the track to examine the engine and coaches. 'I've got to submit reports . . . .'

'How's the bike?' I yelled from the bridge.

'Flattened,' he said with undisguised pleasure. 'You'll never ride that again.'

He couldn't have spoken a truer word. It was a mangled mess of metal and wire and Jonathan was weeping with his arm about his wife. All his work had been ruined. It looked irretrievable. I doubted whether he would ever make another prototype of a fully automatic pedal cycle gear-changing mechanism.

'I'll collect it when you've gone,' I told the engine-driver, giving him my name. 'No one's hurt . . . .'

'And my engine's not damaged either. Bloody stupid people, what the hell was he doing?'

'Trying to make history,' I said limply.

But Jonathan did not make history.

I said I did not want any cash for my ruined machine, he could keep it if he wished, so that he could continue his work on the automatic cycle gear system, but he said the damage was so great that repair was impossible. To reconstruct it to the detail he had originally incorporated was beyond even him – he could not remember the necessary detail and his plans would not help, so he said, but I think he just gave up that idea.

The last time I saw him, he was working on a type of side-saddle for ladies who wished to ride bikes while wearing skirts. He believed the age of elegance had not yet passed and in honour of his faithful wife, he would call it a Daisy Newbould; Daisy thought it was a wonderful idea.

I said he was welcome to use the remains of my old bike for that prototype too, and said he could help himself to the bits from the village tip, and I even offered to come and observe the first testing of the new side-saddle cycle.

But I never saw that invention in action.

7 Ain't Misbehaving

Conduct is three-fourths of our life and its
largest concern.
Matthew Arnold (1822–88)

The way we behave in public has long been subjected to rules
and regulations; the church has issued its guidance, the law
has imposed additional restrictions and society itself has
created its own manners and modes of acceptable conduct.

In the privacy of our own homes, however, we can virtually
do as we like, albeit with some exceptions such as making too
much noise or keeping dangerous animals. At home, for
example, we can drop litter on the floor and leave it there; we
needn't clean the windows or polish the brasses if we don't
want to and we needn't clean ourselves either. We can wear
what clothes we want, or dress in nothing at all if we so desire.
We can be awkward or even downright nasty with our family
and friends, we can use filthy language towards them, the sort
that might result in a fine if used in a public place, and we
need never to wash the crockery or dust the interior. In other
words, we can live like pigs if we want to.

There is no law to say we must buy furniture, make our
beds every morning or clean out the bath after using it. There
is nothing to say we must flush our toilets, sweep the carpets
or refrain from keeping coal in the kitchen. There is nothing
to say we must house-train our pets or wash our sweaty
armpits.

As a consequence of this freedom there are, in this lovely
country of ours, a lot of very filthy, smelly and horrible house
interiors which are occupied by equally filthy, smelly and

horrible people. But who is to say that such conduct is wrong? Who may criticize those who live in such conditions if that is their wish, even if those conditions are worse than those endured by many animals? There would be a terrible fuss if some of our zoos or kennels were as filthy as some Englishmen's homes.

Every police officer, doctor, nurse, welfare officer and other person who enters private houses can tell their own horror stories. I've entered houses where the stench made my stomach turn; I've seen filthy living-rooms devoid of all furnishings, other than a massive colour TV set; I've seen cases where repairs were never done and dirt never cleaned away – and most of these miserable homes were due only to idleness. Many of the menfolk earned good money, but spent it in the pub or on the horses, many of the women spent all morning in bed asleep instead of caring for the family home . . . rarely was there any social deprivation in such cases, just plain stupidity aided by mammoth attacks of idleness. Lack of money is no excuse for low-class living standards. It costs nowt to keep one's home or oneself clean.

One strange example I came across involved an old man who stored his own urine in milk bottles. He kept pint bottles of old urine all over the house. They lined the stairs, filled the floors of all five bedrooms save for a narrow path to his own bed, covered the floors of all rooms on the ground floor, occupied every shelf in the place, every corner and every cupboard.

There must have been hundreds of gallons of the stuff and the place stank, of course; it was nauseating but so far as I know, he was not breaking any criminal law. If he wanted to keep his own precious pee in an open-topped milk bottle, why shouldn't he?

I'm not sure the milkman would have approved, but I never did discover why he adopted this course. I did wonder if his ancestors had sold their urine to the local alum industry – years ago, men could sell a barrel of human urine for eight pence, a considerable sum at that time, for it was one of the raw ingredients used in the manufacture of alum crystals, along with alum shale and ash from burnt seaweed. Barrels of urine were collected locally or even brought from as far as London. Perhaps that old man's long-dead family had once been major suppliers and he, like them, had been reared to conserve all his natural water?

Private behaviour of the sort which would be unsocial if conducted in public, is not always a surprise or a shock when one knows the people involved. None the less, there can be surprises. The poorest and untidiest old woman can keep an immaculate house, or the most sophisticated of people can live in the midst of ordure.

During one's duty when dealing with the public in their own homes, therefore, there are always surprises and any police officer can experience a rather unexpected jolt when entering another person's house. Quite often, the exterior of the house, or the standing of the person in the community, bears no relation to their secret life indoors. It was a shock of this kind that greeted me when I paid a visit to the home of Mr Greville Beecham.

Greville lived alone in a large roomy country house set in its own grounds along the Elsinby road, about half a mile outside Aidensfield. It was called Beecham Hall and had been the family home for generations, Greville being descended from the aristocracy, but during this century most of the land had been sold to neighbouring farmers which had left Greville with some two acres, in the middle of which was the magnificent house on its lofty site. He enjoyed a private income from the past investments of his ancestors and had interests in several large department stores in Leeds, York and Hull. He was a director of several companies and was regarded as an expert share dealer by members of the Stock Exchange.

Greville had never married and lived a somewhat solitary home life, although he did seem to have a fairly active public life. On regular occasions, he would drive out of the village in his old Bentley car to attend to business and social matters.

In addition to being a member of the county council, he was chairman of various local organizations, such as the British Legion, the Aidensfield Historical Society and the parish council. Greville was considered a useful fellow to have on a committee and was a member of several. He was also very generous towards local and national charities.

Intelligent, charming and popular, he was respected and liked by everyone who knew him, including myself. An impressive figure in his middle forties, he was some six feet three inches tall with powerful shoulders and a handsome, slender figure. He had a very healthy looking clean-shaven face with clear pink skin, blue eyes and a head of thinning fair hair; he was, I suppose, a modern example of what a Viking warrior might have looked like and I was surprised he had never been captured by a good-looking woman. He was always smartly dressed in expensive clothes which had a rural appearance – tweedy suits or checked sports jackets and cavalry twill trousers, brogue shoes and thick, woollen socks. He was a stylish man, the sort who would turn heads at any gathering.

I had met him at various village events and had always found him courteous, charming and warm but, as the months passed, I realized he never invited people into his home. On the other hand, Greville received plenty of invitations to dinner, often in the homes of the local aristocracy but also to the homes of local business and professional people.

But, being a bachelor, he never returned their hospitality by inviting them to Beecham Hall. If he wanted to entertain anyone, he booked a table in one or other of the best local hotels or restaurants. People were not surprised – after all, Greville was a man, he had no wife or resident cook, and so they understood. Or they thought they understood.

That was my understanding of his life style until I made an unannounced visit to Beecham Hall. I had had no cause to visit Greville until the locality suffered a spate of night-time attacks on local licensed premises. A team was touring the north-east of England and raiding village pubs by gaining entry through the cellar flaps. They were stealing large quantities of spirits, cigarettes and, in some cases, cash from the tills in those establishments where the landlords had not emptied the drawers after the night's business. A vehicle was being used – no one could carry off heavy cases of whisky or brandy or large cartons of cigarettes without some form of transport and so we circulated warnings to all the local pubs.

The means of entry was usually the cellar flap, this being prized open with a crowbar or similar tool, although in some cases the back door had been forced.

I warned the landlords and proprietors of all the inns on my beat, including George Ward, and asked them if I might inspect their cellars, rear doors and windows to offer security advice. In George's case, the cellar flap was practically useless.

When the twin coverings were closed, they were bolted from the inside, but the wood surrounds into which the bolts slotted were old and rotten. It was possible to move them by hand – thus it was an easy matter to force open the cellar flap from the outside and enter via the short wooden ladder. I advised George to replace the old woodwork and make the flap more secure. He assured me that he would.

But he didn't. One night, someone forced open the flap and removed several crates of whisky, brandy and gin, six crates of beer, ten cartons of cigarettes, umpteen boxes of potato crisps and £87 cash from the till. George was furious and so was I.

'I thought you'd warned your landlords, Rhea?' snapped Sergeant Blaketon down the telephone when I reported the crime to him. 'This one sounds easy pickings to me.'

'I did warn George, Sergeant, I inspected his cellar and his doors and windows and advised him to make them more secure . . . .'

'We want this lot caught, Rhea,' he said. 'Making fools of us, raiding our pubs at night, you should have been alert to this possibility . . . .'

'Yes, Sergeant.' I listened as he rambled on and promised I would do my best to trace the culprits. Later that morning, a farmer rang my home and left a message with my wife. He had found some discarded whisky and brandy cartons on his land, and I got the message at lunch-time.

When I inspected the boxes, I asked George to have a look at them and he nodded.

'They're from my cellar,' he said. 'I recognize them, that's got my mark on it, after I'd checked it over on receipt. See? G.W. My initials. I wrote it. It means I checked the contents and found everything correct. So why dump the empty boxes here?'

'To get rid of the evidence, George. One bottle of whisky's just like another and they know that. So having got rid of this evidence, if they'd got stopped after leaving here, who could say they'd stolen the booze they carried in the car? There's nothing to say where their whisky came from, is there? If it had still been in those cartons, though, and we'd stopped them for a check, we would have known where it had come from. We could have proved they'd done it. They're professionals, they must have spotted your initials on the boxes and decided to get rid of the evidence.'

'Bastards,' said George.

As I looked around, I realized that, to reach this out-of-the-way dumping place, the vehicle must have driven along a lane which ran below Beecham Hall; the Hall was perched on the hilltop and the lane skirted the hill directly beneath it to emerge in Thackerston. I decided to ask the householders along the route if they had heard or seen any activity during the night. And the most obvious house at which to begin was Beecham Hall.

When I rang the bell, Greville answered. He was dressed in casual slacks, a T-shirt and sandals and smiled a welcome.

'Hello, PC Rhea, come in,' and he held the huge door open as I stepped into the rather dark entrance hall. As I followed him into the depths of the building in very dim light, I was vaguely aware of a cluttered route, but he said, 'In there,' and pointed to a door on my right.

'Excuse the mess,' he said as he pushed open the door. 'Find a chair if you can. I'll make some coffee. You've time for one?'

'Yes,' I said, realizing he'd not given me time to explain the purpose of my visit, then as he went off to the kitchen, I entered the room, conscious only of its overwhelming darkness. The thick curtains were drawn across the bay window to omit most of the day's sunshine, but as my eyes grew accustomed to the gloom, I saw the room was piled high with rubbish which had all the appearances of being dumped and not arranged in any way. It was like a tatty second-hand dealer's junk-shop – cheap old furniture, tables, picture-frames, mangles, curtains, rugs and clothing, chairs, beds and old mattresses . . . there was a total lack of order in the room, everything was piled high, one thing being thrown on top of another without any attempt to stack it neatly. There were old cardboard boxes full of cracked crockery, mirrors, books galore, old newspapers and magazines. But this was not good stuff, it was rubbish, junk, cheap cast-offs.

As I stood in the midst of this offal, I looked around for a chair, but the only ones were battered old dining-chairs which had seen better days in some small kitchen. I dragged one from beneath a table, removed a pile of old newspapers from it, dusted the seat with an old sweater I found on the floor, and sat upon it to examine the room with more care. As I waited, Greville came in with two mugs of coffee, handed me one and pulled himself a chair from the mess.

'Sorry about the mess,' he said. 'I keep meaning to tidy up but, well, you know how it is.'

I murmured something which I hoped was a show of understanding but he made no attempt to explain the reason for this room full of junk.

'So, what brings the constabulary here?' he smiled. Unlike his house, he was clean and well groomed, even when relaxing.

I told him about the raid on the pub and how I thought the thieves had driven along the lane below his house sometime during the night, then asked if he'd heard anything.

'Come through to the dining-room,' he said. 'It overlooks that lane. Bring your coffee. Yes, I did hear a car last night, or in the early hours.'

The dining-room, at the other side of the dusty, cramped hall, was just as bad as the lounge, littered almost to the ceiling with further loads of utter junk.

The heavy curtains were drawn too but I could distinguish the piles of clutter, a repetition of what was stored in the lounge. He drew back a curtain and pointed.

'Down there, Mr Rhea, you see the old barn? The track comes past it, well, I can see that view from my bedroom, directly above this room. And in the early hours, three o'clock I'd say, I did see car lights down there. I was awake, I'd got indigestion, I dined with friends last night, so I got up to take something to ease it and noticed the lights.'

'Can you give me any idea what sort of car it was? Who was with it? Anything?'

'Sorry, no. I heard doors banging but that's all, then it drove off, towards Thackerston. Sorry I can't be more precise.'

'Thanks, Mr Beecham,' I said. 'It's a start. I'm visiting all the houses along here, to see if anyone can describe the car.'

'I hope you find the crooks,' he said, leading me from the room. I left my coffee mug on a dusty old table in the hall, thanked him and left. Outside, the mansion looked splendid, a fine house some 250 years old with mullioned windows, a fine portico and superb views. But inside, it was no better furnished than an itinerant scrap-dealer's caravan.

We never traced those who had broken into the pub and I never did find out why such a wealthy, personable and generous character like Greville Beecham lived in such utter squalor.

Many of us have heard the old joke about Queen Elizabeth I who said she made sure she had a bath at least once a month, whether or not she needed one. There were people like that in and around Aidensfield. One was an old fellow who always wore his flat cap, even when sitting in the bath and even when washing his face at other times. In fact, his wife swore he never actually washed his face – he just rubbed it with dry hands and made appropriate washing noises with his mouth.

Another was a fish seller who operated a weekly stall in Ashfordly on market day but who, for the rest of the week, was a chimney-sweep. He spent his week getting blacker and blacker and looked an oddity when serving fresh fish from behind his stall, for he never seemed to be clean and the combination of smells which surrounded him were extremely pungent, especially in high summer.

It was his boast that he was so busy that he had only one night out – that was the last Saturday of every month when he attended a working men's club in Eltering. And, in preparation, he got a bath on the Wednesday previous to that.

But it was a bathing problem that brought hilarity, with some later sadness, to Elsinby early one summer. A lady called Sybil Cornforth lived in a bungalow behind the high street. In her late sixties, she was the widow of a former fireman and had returned to live in the village upon the death of her husband, having been born and reared here in childhood; she'd been educated in Elsinby primary school.

She was a jolly woman, the life and soul of any party and she had a wonderful and infectious sense of humour. She took a very active part in Elsinby WI, the parochial church council and a wide range of village hall fund-raising events. She was also a leading member of the parish church choir, for she had a beautiful contralto voice and could move an audience to tears by the quality of her singing.

Everyone loved Sybil, and she had lots of visitors and friends, including an army of nieces and nephews who lived nearby. Sybil was a very distinctive lady, however, for she must have weighed some 22 stone. She was truly enormous, with a multitude of chins, a back as wide as that of a carthorse, a waist the size of a fully grown cow and legs like the trunk of a centuries-old oak tree.

She fairly waddled down the street but was always laughing and joking, making fun of her own size and chuckling at her lack of mobility. She had tried to slim but all her efforts had failed, and she made light of the fact that she could not sit in a conventional single cinema seat and that her own chairs were specially built to accommodate her broad backside and huge weight.

Sybil's daily routine in Elsinby was fairly well known. She would rise around 7.30 a.m., take in her milk and prepare her own breakfast. Then, around 9.30 a.m., she would potter down to the shop for her morning paper, her daily groceries and other requirements.

While in the village, she would sometimes call on friends for coffee or visit others to discuss parish church matters or something connected with fund-raising at the village hall. She was always active, always doing something or calling somewhere, therefore she was a very regular sight around Elsinby.

When she failed to take in her milk one morning, therefore, and then failed to appear in the shop at the expected time, there was immediate concern.

Neighbours knocked and shouted at her door, but without response, and by ten o'clock, someone rang me. I rushed down to Elsinby to find a knot of villagers hanging about outside Sybil's door. They burst into an anxious chatter at my approach – I noticed the full milk bottle on the doorstep as I sought a spokesman. John Oakley, who lived next door, came forward.

'You've tried all the doors?' I asked. 'Bedroom window?'

'Aye,' he said with sadness in his voice. 'Shouted through t'letter-box, hammered on t'doors, back and front, knocked on her bedroom window. Her curtains are still drawn, bedroom and front room, I fear she's not got out o' bed, Mr Rhea . . . .'

I knew what they were thinking. They thought Sybil had died during the night and I was now faced with a decision as to whether or not to break in. If she was still in bed, having a sleep in, it would be a gross intrusion if I smashed my way in, but surely the loud knocking and persistent shouting by her neighbours would have aroused her?

'She never sleeps in, Mr Rhea,' said John as if reading my mind.

'OK, I'll go in,' I said.

The easiest way to break into a house, as any burglar will testify, is to smash a ground floor window close to the catch, reach in and open the window. It is then possible to climb through and so I found a stone in her garden, crashed it against the glass of her bedroom window, released the catch and hauled it open. It was a matter of a moment to climb in.

The others waited outside, not wishing to be confronted with death and so I did not open her curtains. I left them closed as I fought my way behind them, but when I saw her bed, it was empty. It had been slept in, however, for the sheets and blankets were turned back as if someone had climbed out.

'Sybil?' I shouted, looking on the floor beyond the bed. 'Sybil? Are you there?'

Beyond the bedroom, I heard a faint noise and went into the passage to investigate; the bathroom adjoined through one door, and there was a small toilet through another. The toilet door was open, and it was unoccupied.

'Sybil?' I hesitated at the bathroom door, not wishing to

intrude upon a lady if she was bathing, and called her name.
'Sybil?'

There was a faint response from inside, a hoarse groan
almost and I identified it as a call of distress. I had to go in.

Fortunately, she had not locked the door but when I pushed
it open, I was confronted by a grotesque sight. Sybil was lying
on her back in the bath, stark naked with both arms sticking
up like flagpoles and both legs hanging over a tiny stool which
lay on its side under her knees. Her mountain of flesh filled the
whole bath, with colossal breasts and huge wedges of stomach
and thigh seeming to dominate the scene. But she was alive
and her eyes were filled with a mixture of relief and
embarrassment at my arrival.

'Sybil!' I hurried to her. Her mouth was trying to tell me
something but she was hoarse and no words would come. I
could see what had happened. She was stuck in the bath. I was
later to learn, that because of her size, she could not sit in the
bath but always used a small footstool to sit upon. She filled
the bath with water and sat on the stool to wash herself all
over, but on this occasion she had reached for the soap behind
her and the stool had overbalanced. It had slid forward to
throw her off, and she had fallen backwards into the bath,
causing a huge overflow onto the bathroom floor. Her huge
size and enormous weight had wedged her in, and her arms
had been similarly wedged skywards so that she could not
lower them. The stool had remained in the bath, under her
knees, and thus she was firmly wedged in place. She couldn't
lower her arms or hands to lever herself out but had managed
to dislodge the plug with one of her toes. The bathwater had
drained out, fortunately, but she was very cold none the less.

She had lain there since seven o'clock that morning,
shouting and even singing loudly until she had lost her voice –
and although she had heard the knocking and shouting, she'd
been unable to attract attention to her plight.

But all that information came later. The immediate problem
for me was to get her out of the bath and to somehow preserve
her modesty. I managed to remove the stool from beneath her
tree-like legs which provided some relief, then went into the
bedroom and took a couple of blankets off the bed to cover her

as I decided how to tackle this weighty problem.

I unlocked the back door to tell the assembled small crowd of well-wishers that she was safe and well while explaining the problem. I then asked Jean, the wife of her neighbour John Oakley, if she would mind staying with Sybil as a form of feminine safeguard against any accusations that others might level against John and I. People did do that sort of thing – they could create wild rumours about a man or men being alone with a naked woman, even if she was gigantic and stuck in the bath and even if we were on a rescue mission.

As Jean went into the bathroom to comfort Sybil, John and I settled down to discuss the logistics of our problem. Whatever way we examined the situation, it seemed the only way that Sybil could be extricated was by human muscle power. Mobile cranes and motor-car lifting equipment could not be utilized without knocking down the bathroom walls.

We did consider ringing the vet who had some equipment for hoisting cattle and horses out of quagmires. Then John suggested filling the bath. He reckoned the water would add some buoyancy, however small, to the bulk of female flesh which was trapped therein and so we suggested that to Sybil, exhorting her not to try to lower her arms. We didn't want to have to grapple with slippery bits and needed both arms to be kept dry – not that she could have lowered them anyway. They were still sticking upright like flagpoles.

Sybil agreed to the water treatment so long as the water was warm. Jean opened the tap and ran it until warm water emerged, fitted the plug and began to fill the bath. Sybil retained her shroud which was soaked as the water rose almost to the brim, covering her legs and bubbling around the bulk which was the cause of the problem.

'Right,' said John. 'Nick, if you stand on t'edge of t'bath, on t'rim, at one side and me at t'other, against t'wall, and then we take hold of her arms, one apiece, and lift, we might shift her. If she can push against t'tap end wiv her feet at t'same time, we might git her moving . . . .'

We tried that arrangement. She was so heavy I was frightened I would pull her arm out of its socket, but she could not reach the tap end with her feet to give us extra help. We heaved, puffed and panted, shouted and hauled at those long fat arms, but she wouldn't move.

'If we replaced the stool to the tap end,' I suggested, 'she could push against that . . . .'

The stool was placed in the bath, on its side, and Sybil said, by bending her knees, she could obtain a lot of leverage against it.

'If we heave on your arms as you push against that stool with your feet,' I said, 'we might win.'

It worked. With an enormous heave, Sybil thrust her weight against the stool as we heaved on her arms, and with a slushing of water, the mass of flesh shifted towards the head of the bath. She was free. Gently, she edged backwards – and then knocked John.

He tried to retain his balance in the cramped space on the edge of the bath, lost his footing and slithered into the bath, landing on top of Sybil. With a screeching of bare flesh on the enamel, Sybil shot forward again with John on board but, with legs outstretched, she halted their joint slither by planting her feet against the submerged stool. John managed to clamber off the white-shrouded, wet mass of wobbly flesh and, without any further help from us, Sybil struggled to her feet, hugging the wet sheet around her.

But she was free. The drama was over and we left the scene of our triumph, leaving Sybil to get dressed.

'Wait before you go, I'll make some coffee,' she called to us, and so we went into the kitchen.

As we waited, I thought about Jonathan Newbould (see chapter 6), the village inventor and wondered if he could make a non-slip stool which would make a secure perch for Sybil when coping with her bath. Perhaps he could fit rubber suckers to its feet? Or perhaps manufacturers of baths could produce a device for aiding large or even handicapped people to sit in comfort and safety while washing? Or would a showerbath be more feasible for Sybil?

Afterwards, Sybil laughed and joked with everyone about her experience, telling her friends in the village how she'd been stuck in the bath with John Oakley. It was John who blushed when being reminded of the incident, not Sybil.

She enjoyed a total lack of embarrassment about her predicament, making fun of her experience wherever she went, and everyone loved her a little more just for that.

Another example of a curious way of living involved a pair of maidenly twin sisters, the Misses Mandeville, Audrey and Rosemary. They had reached that stage of life where they did not wish anyone to know their ages but those of us with reasonable powers of observation would realize that, between them they had scored a century and perhaps a little extra. They were not identical in appearance, Miss Audrey being taller and slightly more slender than her sister. Each had neat greyish-brown hair, spectacles and a rather pale complexion with brown eyes and a rounded, pleasant face.

They dressed smartly in good quality clothes, although their outfits were perhaps a little old-fashioned, and they favoured the more subdued colours such as browns, greens and greys.

They lived in identical bungalows which had been built by their father especially for them; their neat homes stood next to each other and overlooked the village green at Slemmington. Both bungalows were built of local stone with red pantile roofs and they enjoyed delightful gardens behind beech hedges and white gates. Both bungalows were neatly painted with white woodwork and were beautifully maintained; each sister had a small Morris mini car and each enjoyed a private, if modest income as directors of the family's ceramics business.

Each had, in her younger days, worked for a living, Audrey being a solicitor's clerk while Rosemary worked for the civil service. Each had retired early shortly before the death of their father because he had wanted them to become involved with the business he had founded; they were now involved in his business, although a brother was managing director, but they did live quite well, thanks to the legacy provided by their father. He had died some four or five years before my arrival at Aidensfield.

The sisters were quite charming although some considered them rather aloof; various people interpreted their aloofness as an indication of their pretended superiority, but I think it came from their natural reticence, each being rather shy.

Possibly because of their natural reserve, they did not take a very active part in village affairs, although they could be relied upon to give prizes for raffles or jars of honey and jam for garden fêtes, or to provide bunches of flowers for the parish church and useful work for bob-a-job boy scouts. Unlike so many spinsterish sisters, they were not antagonistic towards one another and did spend a good deal of their spare time together, perhaps on a shopping expedition or even on a weekend holiday to the Lake District or in the Scottish Highlands.

But underneath this aura of respectability and family rapport, there was some rivalry. It was a long time before I became aware of this.

England is rich with tales of sisterly rivalry, my own county of Yorkshire boasting two wealthy and warring sisters who could not agree where to build a church for the village, and so each built a church of her own. The village thereafter was embarrassed by having two fine churches. In another case, one sister built a church on the site she had chosen while her sister built the tower on her selected site – the result being that the tower was a long way from the church.

But the Mandeville sisters had not fallen out in such a silly and public way; their rivalry was of a very domestic and private nature. Upon reflection, I suspect that few villagers were aware of any domestic undercurrent between them for it was not the sort of rivalry that would become public knowledge.

I learned about it when Miss Rosemary received a clandestine visit from a housebreaker.

One Monday afternoon, Rosemary had driven into Eltering to visit her bank manager and when she returned at four o'clock, she found she had had an uninvited guest. He had broken a glass panel of the kitchen door at the back of the house, turned the key which she'd left in the lock and had then let himself in to ransack the bungalow, stealing precious ceramics, glassware, some portable antiques such as figurines, vases and candlesticks, some original watercolours and some miniature oil paintings of South American birdlife. A vehicle must have been employed to carry off the loot for it was a daring daylight raid. And no one saw anything suspicious.

It was her sister, Audrey, who rang me and I promised immediate attention, exhorting the women not to touch anything and to leave things exactly as they were until the arrival of our Scenes of Crime Officers. Some victims of burglars and housebreakers would tidy up the house and dust the surfaces before the arrival of the CID – thus destroying any evidence that might have lingered. Before leaving for Slemmington, I rang the divisional office to arrange a visit by SOCO and then hurried to the scene. I found them both in Audrey's bungalow, Rosemary being comforted by her sister with a cup of tea. They assured me that nothing had been touched or moved, and that they had not cleaned the house prior to my visit.

Then I asked them to show me the damage. I added that I'd need a list of everything that had been stolen with detailed descriptions of the missing items. At that early stage, Rosemary was unable to provide such a list and I asked her to wait until SOCO had examined the bungalow for fingerprints and other evidence; I also felt that after waiting for that couple of hours or so she would have recovered her composure sufficiently to cope with making a comprehensive list. Once I had that list, I could circulate descriptions of the stolen goods to all police forces, and local antique dealers could be alerted to the fact that the thief might try to dispose of his ill-gotten gains.

When Detective Sergeant Thornton and his SOCO team had concluded their work, I asked Miss Rosemary to compile that list for me, asking her to be as accurate as possible because the sooner we circulated the list, the better were the chances of locating the thief. I knew she would not be able to make a comprehensive list because, in the days and weeks which followed, she would begin to realize that other objects had vanished. People would never miss a certain object until many weeks later when they wanted it for a particular purpose. But we did urgently need a working list with which to begin our circulation and so Rosemary, with Audrey in close attendance, began to examine her invaded home. It was then that I began to appreciate the sisterly rivalry.

'Two brass candlesticks have gone,' Rosemary's sadness

was evident in her voice. 'From the hall, they were on the piano.'

'What size?' I was making a list in my pocket-book, later to be typed and itemized.

'Ten inches tall,' she said without hesitation.

'No,' sister Audrey butted in. 'I've got the ten-inch ones, yours were the smaller ones, eight inches tall, less valuable, of course. Father gave me the better ones. Rosemary's weren't worth a lot – perhaps £15.'

'But I got the original of Pott's painting of Rievaulx Abbey and that's been taken. It's in oil, in a gilt frame and shows the abbey in springtime, with bluebells in the foreground,' Rosemary beamed at me.

I was surprised at the fierce glow of pride in her face as she added, 'Audrey only got a print of it. No discerning thief would steal a print.'

'Was it valuable, the painting?' I asked.

'Yes, I'd estimate it at around £200,' she smiled. 'The print is only worth a few pounds.'

'If the print is an exact copy of the same picture, our photographic department might reproduce it for circulation,' I said.

And so we went through her home, listing all the items known to be missing and I began to smile to myself as the sisters vied for ownership of the most valuable items.

As I worked, I gained the impression that their father had tried very hard to make them equal, even to the extent of giving copies of pictures to one while giving the original to the other. Thus Rosemary had some originals, Audrey had others; I reckoned they had roughly the same proportion of each. Some of Rosemary's china ornaments were larger or more valuable than Audrey's and some were not, but as I progressed about my work, I found it quite hilarious listening to each woman trying to claim the better ornaments and furnishings. Rosemary kept trying to say that the objects stolen from her home were of far better quality than their counterparts in Audrey's possession. As we progressed through the bungalow, the claims grew stronger and the sisters grew more agitated as each new loss was discovered, each trying to claim they owned the most valuable example.

It was inevitable that Rosemary should come to the conclusion that the burglar must have first examined the contents of Audrey's house before deciding to ignore them in favour of her far superior belongings. She even reached the stage when she was beginning to grow proud of her experience, pleased that the housebreaker had selected her property.

'He's clearly a man of knowledge and discernment,' Rosemary told her sister. 'I think he rejected your stuff because mine was far more valuable. Consider the objects he's taken, not one of them is cheap rubbish. It's all top quality antiques and ceramics.'

'That's being silly!' was the retort.

'No it's not. Really, Audrey, I can't see any self-respecting burglar even thinking of robbing you.'

Audrey responded, 'The man's a moron, Rosemary, and you know it. He's gone for kitsch, he'll sell your stuff on seaside junk stalls and in flea markets, the fellow lacks knowledge of real quality, otherwise he'd have raided my home.'

I let them ramble on, each trying to score points over the other as I made my notes, marking those items which were duplicated in Audrey's home and which we could photograph for police circulars, and I tried not to make any remarks which would allow the women to score points over one another. But it was a strange experience, hearing a woman boasting that her burglar was a man of superior quality.

A week later, Audrey's bungalow was raided and the MO suggested the culprit was the same man. I was pleased that Phil Bellamy was available to deal with that case.

Then I wondered whether they'd each claim to have been visited by the best policeman!

8   Of Creatures Beloved

I think I could turn and live with animals,
they are so placid and self contain'd.
Walt Whitman (1819–92)

From time to time during my constabulary duties at
Aidensfield, I had trouble with a succession of donkeys that
lived upon the dubious generosity of Claude Jeremiah
Greengrass. He seemed to assemble a menagerie of assorted
mokes with personality defects or emotional problems; many
had been abandoned or were unwanted by other carers. They
were sometimes aged and infirm donkeys whose duties on
Strensford Beach were over, although many were young ones
who seemed to have moods varying between outright anger
and sheer stupidity.

I was never quite sure why he took them into shelter. He
maintained it was his love of animals combined with a natural
streak of generosity; he said he did not want to see
hard-worked donkeys end their lives in misery and, to be fair
to Claude, he did care for them and did show them love and
compassion. They were well fed when in his care, their hooves
and coats were tended and there was shelter of sorts in one or
other of his tumbledown outbuildings. I must admit that most
of his donkeys appeared to be quite happy but I was never sure
what happened to them when their contented Greengrass days
were over. They just seemed to fade from the landscape.

From time to time, however, he would gather a younger and
very frisky animal into his care. Quite often, this was a stallion
with a strong sense of desire to breed with anything on four
legs. This did not please the neighbours because one source of

annoyance was the stallions' habit of braying extremely loudly. Their terrible din, a sort of hee-hawing mixed with massive intakes of air and bouts of wheezing like a farrier's bellows, was said by some to be a means of communication with other neighbourhood donkeys and said by others to be an amorous love-song, a sort of donkey serenade. It might have been nothing more than a means of letting people know the donkeys were there and in need of companionship, because donkeys are sociable animals and love the companionship of their own kind, as well as that of humans, horses or other animals. Their habit of braying loudly, as in the case of the Greengrass stallions, might have been their way of protesting about the behaviour of their wily master or his lurcher dog, Alfred; Alfred would sometimes hitch a lift on the back of an unwilling donkey. The dog would stand astride the cross-marked back of the donkey and would defy all attempts by the donkey to throw him off. In some ways, Alfred was quite a showman – some reckoned he had a touch of the circus in his blood.

The most recent addition to the Greengrass stable, a lively stallion called Basil, caused further disturbance in and around Aidensfield because he constantly and noisily fell in love with lady ponies.

He appeared to prefer them to female donkeys and lost no opportunity in making his odd desire known far and wide. It was fortunate for him, but unfortunate for the ponies and their riders, that there were lots of pony mares in the district upon whom Basil could lavish his unrequited love. It is known, of course, that donkeys and horses will cross breed to produce hybrids called mules but this riveting piece of natural history was of little consequence to the pony owners and riders with whose mounts Basil fell headlong and hopelessly in love.

He had found a way of escaping from the Greengrass ranch, apparently through a piece of loose fencing, and once free would pursue the object of his lust through the lanes, woods, fields and villages until he had achieved his purpose. He would ignore the whips, feet and shouts of the riders as he tried, from time to time, to consummate his passion with the pony rider still in the saddle. Little girls received stern warnings about

Basil's activities and were told that if Basil appeared on the scene with a glint in his eye, the girl and her pony should gallop for shelter in the nearest donkey-proof building. Some did wonder why, if Alfred the lurcher could ride upon a donkey, why couldn't a donkey try to ride upon a pony? Parents did not have an easy time explaining Basil's public passion to girls of tender years, although it was evident that some did quickly learn the facts of life, even if it was through regularly witnessing the unashamed actions of a lovesick and very lusty donkey.

Because he could be a confounded nuisance to pony riders as well as a danger to motor traffic, I found myself repeatedly warning Claude Jeremiah Greengrass that he faced prosecution for allowing livestock (i.e. the donkey) to stray upon the highway, or that I might even book him for obstructing the highway and that he might find Basil impounded. Claude did make an effort of sorts, but Basil could defy everyone – when he wanted love and adventure, no one could stop him. If his passion was aroused, no compound could detain him and he was quite capable of leaping a five-bar gate if a desirable pony chanced to wander by.

A fine example of Basil's precociousness occurred one Wednesday morning when I received a call of desperation from the vicar, the Reverend Roger Clifton.

'Nick,' he panted. 'I've just dashed in from the street, I'm ringing from the vicarage, there's rather an embarrassing, er, well, demonstration going on down here. It involves that donkey of Mr Greengrass's.'

I groaned.

'Have you rung him?' was my first question.

'Yes, but there's no reply.'

'So what's the donkey doing now?'

'It's got a pony, a female I suspect, cornered in the lychgate of my church and, well, not to put too fine a point on it, it's trying to mount the pony. The donkey is in, well a high and well advanced state of passion, if you understand.'

'It always is,' I groaned.

'Yes, but this time it's especially embarrassing . . . .'

'You've tried chasing it off?'

'It bares its teeth at me or anyone else who approaches, and, well, it is in a very rampant state. It could be dangerous, Nick, the donkey gets very angry when anyone tries to chase it away from its desired intention, but this situation is rather worse than normal, actually . . . .'

'Worse? Why?'

'That funeral of Mr Tomlinson, he died at Strensford earlier this week and expressed a desire to be buried here. Well, the cortège has just arrived and we can't get the coffin or the mourners into the church or even into the churchyard. The donkey's in the gateway, you see, and it's got a pony cornered there; it is all so very embarrassing with its massive private parts on display, and panting all over the pony as the mourners don't know where to look . . . .'

'Who does the pony belong to?'

'Fiona Lambton. She had hired it to a young girl called Molly Forster, but when the donkey made its overtures, Molly ran home and left the pony to its fate. The pony's not saddled up although it has a halter on . . . I've rung Miss Lambton too, she's not at home either and, well, the mourners are getting a bit restless and the donkey won't stop, it just keeps trying, Nick, and failing, I might add. The more it fails, the more determined it becomes. The poor pony doesn't like it either.'

I promised I would attend immediately and decided to walk down to the church rather than drive; at least that would give me a few minutes longer to try and think of a suitable course of action. I must admit that, as I paraded down the village street in my police uniform, I did not think that the image of the constabulary in action was enhanced by having to cope with a rampant and shameless donkey whose lustful intention was so blatantly obvious.

When I arrived, the cortège was stationary and all the mourners were still seated in the shining black cars with suitably glum expressions on their faces while trying not to look at the romantic natural scene being played out before their very eyes. The undertaker had left his place in the passenger seat of the hearse and was wiping his perspiring brow with a huge white handkerchief, while the vicar stood within the safety of the churchyard. And, tucked beneath the sheltering archway of the lychgate was Basil, as rampant as ever as he tried to mount the whinnying pony which he had managed to detain within the confines of the enclosed gateway. As Basil moved around in a circle, sometimes mounting the pony for the merest of moments before slipping off to try again, the vicar blushed and the undertaker, Josh Durbridge, shouted at the copulators and tried to shoo them away. But Basil bared his teeth at anyone who dared to interrupt his ardour and so no one dared even to attempt to drag him away.

'Thoo'll etti deea summat, Mr Rhea,' Josh wiped his brow again. 'There's some varry straight ladies in yon cars, maiden ladies who've nivver knawn where babies come from let alone how donkey stallions get their kicks, and Ah can't say Ah knaw what effect this'll have on 'em, seeing summat that size. T'vicar might have some bother on his hands when this carry-on's all ovver.'

'One way of treating a man who's a bit rampant, Josh, is to chuck a bucket of cold water over him,' I suggested.

'Or mak him tak a cold shower!' chuckled the undertaker.

'Would it work with a rutting donkey?' I asked. 'A hosepipe? Cold water directed at his tender bits . . . .'

'It's worth a try,' he said.

I went towards Roger Clifton and asked, 'Have you a hosepipe and a water supply? Cold water?'

'Yes, we use it in the churchyard,' he smiled.

'Let's see if we can dampen Basil's ardour,' I suggested.

As Basil continued to exercise his cupidity, we connected a length of hosepipe to a tap in the corner of the churchyard and Josh examined the nozzle.

'We need ti git a fair pressure up,' he said, twisting the nozzle until he seemed satisfied. 'A bit o' power's needed . . . right, Vicar, ton t'tap full on, give it some welly.'

As Josh directed the hose towards the donkey, Roger Clifton turned on the tap and we all waited.

There was a hissing somewhere, the hose wriggled as the water surged through and suddenly a stream of ice-cold water burst from it. Josh aimed it at Basil. But Basil was not going to be deflected from his lasciviousness by a drip of water and as the stream hit him, he ignored it. I knew that Josh was aiming for a certain part of the donkey's anatomy but that was not so easy to achieve in the circumstances and so Josh played the hosepipe over the donkey's back and head, moving it around as he tried to find the centre of Basil's desire and lust.

'It's not makking onny difference!' shouted Josh. 'By, he's a randy awd fussack is yon . . . .'

Then, as Basil slipped off the now soaking object of his passion, the stream of cold water hit the pony in her most sensitive and delicate area. With a sudden whinnying of surprise, she lashed out with her hind legs, kicking Basil in the stomach and knocking him back a few feet, and then she bucked and kicked until she was free. Then, whinnying with embarrassment as Josh continued to play the cold water upon her rear end, the pony twisted like a struggling cat, emerged from the lychgate and galloped away down the village street.

'Well, Ah'll be capped,' said Josh. 'Water off now, Vicar, we've done t'trick.'

But Basil was not going to be outdone. With a deep-throated hee-haw, he set off in pursuit of the pony, his passion not in the least diminished.

I watched in some alarm as the two animals tore headlong down Aidensfield village street, with cars swerving to avoid them. My only consolation was that the funeral was free to go ahead.

'Thanks, Josh,' I said with some gratitude.

Josh beamed at the vicar, 'I reckon that's some kind of baptism, eh?' and then, adopting his solemn funereal mask, turned to the waiting cortège and said, 'We can now convey the departed into the church.'

My problem was the departed pony and donkey. If Basil got his way, he would corner that pony in some other place to continue his interrupted fornication and so I walked briskly away to try and locate the pair of them. But I needn't have worried. The pony managed to find its way into its own stable and Fiona Lambton arrived just in time to slam the door against the advancing Basil.

'What on earth's happened to Sunbeam? She's all wet!'

asked Fiona as Basil frothed at the mouth while head-butting the stable door in the urge to reach the pony.

'She's been rescued from a fate worse than death.' I explained the situation. 'So, can you keep this donkey here until Claude Jeremiah comes for him?'

'He won't go away, I can tell you that,' Fiona said. 'He'll hang about that stable until he's dragged away . . . he'll tackle anything, will that Basil. What a libido! I wish I could find a man like that. Does Claude know he's here?'

'No,' I said. 'Perhaps you'd ring him and ask him to collect his donkey?'

And before she could refuse my request I walked away, relieved to leave the problem in her capable hands.

One of the reasons I left Fiona to cope with Basil was that I had had lots of occasions to threaten legal action against Fiona due to the behaviour of her own horses and ponies. They seemed to cause as much bother as Claude Jeremiah's donkeys and I thought this was one way of repaying her for past bother. (See *Constable on the Hill*.)

Her horses were a fascinating collection. One of them was always ridden to Ashfordly market by Johnny Brown, a local character, and it then found its own way back to Aidensfield. Johnny would return by bus later in the day. This was an example of the ability of some horses to operate without riders and, in the past, many milkmen would rely on the horse to find its way around the village delivery route. The milkman would deliver on foot as the horse took the cart of milk from house to house. There are lots of similar tales about horses carrying drunken owners home, or finding their own way home when their rider had had an accident.

But even in the 1960s, it was not wise to have an unattended horse wandering the country lanes. There were traffic hazards which had not been in existence even forty years earlier, and so a free-ranging horse was a problem.

I was faced with such a worry by one of Fiona Lambton's horses. It was a delightful gelding called Treacle due to his wonderful golden colouring. He was a superb animal who was loved by all who met him, but he had a curious weakness.

Treacle had a passion for fox hunting. On the morning of a hunt meeting, he would begin to shiver with excitement, growing restless and agitated and whinnying for his mistress to come and saddle him up. In the horsebox *en route* to the meet, he continued in this state of high excitement, rattling his hooves on the floor of the trailer or neighing loudly as he approached the meet. And then, when he and Fiona were galloping across the countryside among dozens of other horses and riders, Treacle was in his seventh heaven. For Treacle the horse, hunting was like a drug; he could not exist without his regular dose.

The snag was that Fiona did not attend every meet. Somehow, Treacle knew when there was a local meeting, perhaps due to other horses from Aidensfield being taken there or maybe due to a deep-seated sixth sense. When there was a meet in the district, he would become highly irritable and restless, kicking his stable door or chewing the wood from doors and gates in his frustration. Then one day, he decided that if Fiona would not take him hunting, he would go by himself.

And so he did. He leapt the fences of his home ground to escape just as he leapt the fences when hunting with the other horses.

On the first occasion he hunted alone, no one paid much immediate attention to the unattended horse. The regulars knew it belonged to Fiona Lambton and the fact it bore no harness or saddlery probably meant she was about to correct that defect. But when it galloped off without a rider and followed the hunt to its conclusion with never a sight of Fiona, the master of foxhounds realized he must do something about it.

I was told that he rang Fiona to inform her that her horse had somehow attended the meet, but she did not seem to be very perturbed about it. But when it happened on several further occasions, the MFH decided to take action.

'Look here, Fiona,' Mr Gregory Stanleigh-Prowd telephoned her one Saturday morning, 'This bloody horse of yours has turned up again, we can't have riderless horses going hunting, you know, damned dangerous if you ask me.'

She said he had come to no harm and knew how to conduct himself in the field; if someone would tether him when the hunt was over, she would arrange to collect him.

I was blissfully unaware of Treacle's regular truancy until I received a call from a motorist. A travelling salesman had been driving past Whemmelby Lane end when he'd seen a riderless horse heading into the dale. He called me because he thought the rider might have been thrown off and was perhaps lying injured somewhere. I drove down to Whemmelby only to find the place swarming with huntsmen and women in their finery.

Horse boxes were parked along the verges and there, among the lively horses, I saw Treacle and recognized him instantly. I located Stanleigh-Prowd and asked, 'Mr Stanleigh-Prowd, isn't that Fiona Lambton's horse?'

'Yes, it is, damned thing. It gets out and follows local horses to the meets. See, no saddle, no halter. It follows us everywhere we go.'

'Isn't it dangerous, having a loose horse among you?'

'Normally I'd agree with that, Mr Rhea, but old Treacle is wonderful, he's no bother really, but, well, a riderless horse on the highway isn't exactly a sound idea.'

'It could cause a nasty accident,' I said. 'So after a day's hunting, how does he get home?' I asked.

'He doesn't. He can find his way here all right, by tracking horse boxes, I reckon, but he can't find his way home again. So once the hunt is over, he will hang around near a horse box until someone tethers him. We all know him, fortunately, he's no real trouble.'

'And then Fiona is called?'

'Exactly. She will come to collect him. Bloody thing . . . he's hooked on hunting, you see, Mr Rhea. Very well trained, mind, a fine animal really.'

'Can we tie him up now? Before you ride off? You can leave without him. I'll ring her and ask her to collect him.'

'He would go berserk, Mr Rhea. No, either she rides him or he comes with us now. I'll see to him, between us we'll care for him, the others know him well enough. But we mustn't tie up old Treacle while the others are hunting, God, no!'

'That's a risk, is it?'

'God, yes. He'd do everything in his power to free himself, might even strangle himself while trying to get loose. We couldn't have that, I couldn't take that risk. Imagine, leaving him here, tied up all day while we're riding to hounds within his earshot? He'd go mad.'

'It seems we need to find a rider for him when Fiona can't make it?' I suggested.

'Yes, we tried to suggest that to Fiona, some of our members need a mount from time to time, but she doesn't seem to worry about him. But she'll have to do something, he'll go mad if he's not allowed to hunt with us. Between us, we make sure he doesn't go on any roads.'

I was conscious of the illegality of allowing a horse to stray on the highway and I was equally aware of the dangers of a riderless horse trotting along the country lanes, even if it was as calm and lovely as dear old Treacle. The drivers of cars, lorries and motor cycles might not realize that Treacle was trained to cope with traffic but irrespective of all the arguments in his favour, Treacle could not be allowed to roam by himself.

In spite of Stanleigh-Prowd's assurance, I knew there would be risks and there would be times when Treacle would be on the public roads without a rider.

I called to see Fiona Lambton later that day.

'He's liable to be impounded,' I warned her. 'If our motor patrol come across him while he's riderless, they'll follow standard procedures. He could be locked up, Miss Lambton.'

'Poor old pet,' she mused. 'He does so love hunting, Mr Rhea, he really does. But I can't go to every meet and, well, he insists, you see. I've tried keeping him back . . . he'll kick the stable doors and might injure himself if I keep him in.'

'Couldn't one of your riding pupils go hunting on him if you can't make it?'

'Not really, not if they're not members. And it is expensive, you know, joining the hunt. Few young people can afford it.'

'Can't they join just for the day? Just for one particular outing?'

'Yes, they can, there are day subscriptions. But, well, I seldom know in advance whether or not I can go, you see.

Getting a rider at the last minute, with the necessary funds, well, it's not as simple as it sounds, Mr Rhea.'

'It's your problem, Miss Lambton,' I said. 'And you could be fined or your horse could be impounded or worse still, injured. You must do something to curb his lone wanderings.'

'Yes, of course, Mr Rhea.'

It would be some four or five weeks later when I came across Mr Stanleigh-Prowd in Brantsford. He had been entertaining a business friend to lunch and took the opportunity to stop for a chat. 'You've seen Fiona about that confounded horse?' he put to me.

I explained what I'd done and he nodded. 'Well, she's been out with us since, so there's been no problem, but it will arise again, Mr Rhea, the bloody woman doesn't care, you know. She is a bit blasé about it all.'

'The rule about only members riding with the hunt is a stumbling-block,' I said. 'She has some pupils who could take Treacle hunting otherwise. Some can't afford to join the hunt nor even fork out for single-day subscriptions.'

'We can't have every Tom, Dick and Harriet turning up at our official hunts, you know. There's insurance to consider, the use of farmers' lands, club rules and so on. We do have standards to keep, Mr Rhea, we are reluctant to encourage non-members to ride with us. I agree she couldn't let just any pupil ride Treacle during a hunt.'

Then I had a brain-wave.

'Why not make Treacle a member?' I said. 'In his own right. Then he could hunt, couldn't he? If he was a member, he could hunt with someone other than Fiona Lambton up?'

'Hah!' he chortled. 'What a bloody scheme, Officer! Trust a policeman to find a way around the bloody rule book!'

'It might save the life of a neurotic horse,' I laughed with him. 'And Fiona Lambton can afford his subscription.'

'Bloody hell, whatever next! All right, I'll put it to our committee. A horse a member! Honorary membership perhaps . . . with no voting rights . . . I'll have to see what the rule book says . . .' and he strode off, chortling to himself.

But a week later, Treacle became a member of the Slemmington Hunt, with Fiona paying his annual fee and thus, in theory, anyone could ride him. Fiona made sure that the youngsters who did ride to hounds with him were very capable and thus the Slemmington Hunt had its first four-legged member.

I wondered how he could cope if he was invited to the annual Hunt Ball.

Rather like a rural veterinary surgeon, a country police officer has to deal with many animals, albeit not in a medical sense. More often than not, we are concerned with creatures who are involved with problems or whose owners are involved with problems.

On one occasion, I found myself in Elsinby churchyard because I received a telephone call late one summer evening to say there were suspicious noises coming from the corner under the yew trees. The caller, who'd rung from a kiosk, rang off before I could obtain a name and address, but I felt it sounded like a genuine call.

For some weeks prior to that call, it had been suspected that drunks were using the silence of the graves for an after-hours drinking session and also that vandals were damaging tombstones and memorials. So off I went to investigate the report, fully armed with my trusty torch and truncheon.

When I arrived, everything was in silence. There was not a murmur of wind nor any other sound among the tombstones and although it was not totally dark, it was difficult to see into the deeper recesses of the vegetation or beneath the thick yew trees. I entered the churchyard as quietly as I could, walking on the grass instead of the footpaths, as I began my tour of the tombstones.

I looked behind each headstone, for such memorials did provide an effective hiding place for drinkers and lovers, but I found nothing. There was no one lurking behind the stones, no signs of empty beer bottles or litter and neither did I discover any recent signs of vandalism. But as I made my way towards the darkness of the shadows beneath the yews, I did discern some faint sounds. It was like heavy breathing, a gentle and almost rhythmic noise. I halted and listened. In some ways, it reminded me of slumbering cows. When patrolling at night, the calm sound of the breathing of sleeping cows was one of the noises of the darkness, one which could frighten anyone not accustomed to rural sounds. But this was not a meadow – it was a churchyard, and there should be no cows here.

If it was not a cow, it was probably a drunk sleeping off a heavy session or, of course, it might be a pair of lovers resting after the evening's activities. I crept forward and stooped to peer into the darkness . . . there was something! I halted, hair bristling on the nape of my neck as I tried to see what was lurking there – then I shone my torch.

Two massive eyes blinked back at me . . . a huge beast lumbered to its feet, white face shining in the light of my torch and nostrils extending as it fumed at my stupidity in disturbing its slumbers. It was a bull – and a big one. With the speed of light, it rose to its feet and within seconds was lumbering towards me.

I did not lumber towards the exit. I fled. I galloped. I raced across the churchyard, weaving between the tombstones and sometimes leap-frogging over them as I tried to put distance between myself and the bull. He followed, panting and making curiously frightening noises as I leapt, galloped and fled towards the gate.

The oncoming bull knocked over some tombstones, demolished several vases of flowers and trampled over some shrubbery as it lumbered after me. But I won. I raced out of the gate and locked it behind me, panting like a broken-winded gallower. The bull halted at the other side, gazing at me but unable to follow.

'You bloody vandal!' I shouted at it. Then I wondered who it belonged to.

I'd not seen the bull around the village and so I went to The Hopbind Inn which was still serving and told them of my discovery.

'It'll be Awd Jesse's,' said one of the regulars.

Jesse was Mr Jesse Ramsay of High Farm so I drove there immediately and told him the story. When we searched the field for his bull, it had gone; some hikers had apparently left the gate open and the bull had gone for walkies. Fortunately, the churchyard gate must also have been open and so the bull had wandered in for a rest and a meal of lush grass. I do not know who telephoned me, although I suspect it was one of the careless hikers.

'He's as gentle as a kitten, Mr Rhea,' he told me. 'He wouldn't have hurt you.'

'Tell that to the vicar,' I said. 'He's knocked over a few items of graveyard furniture.'

After daylight next morning, the village was full of rumours about vandals rampaging around the churchyard with the damage being claimed as firm evidence of their activities. But I told the villagers that the rumours were just a load of bull.

Among the other animals which caused problems were Bushy the Border collie, an exploding pig and a kidnapped bufflehead.

Bushy was a lovely dog owned by an Aidensfield lady. He was a Border collie and should have been employed tending sheep, but he was in fact a domestic dog and a much-loved pet. He had a lovely nature and everyone liked him. But he had a curious hobby – he chased aeroplanes.

Other dogs had a propensity for chasing cars or motor-cycles, but Bushy preferred aeroplanes. Just as the car or motor-cycle chasers would run after a passing vehicle, barking at its back wheel for a couple of hundred yards, so Bushy would run along beneath the flight path of a passing plane, barking at it and snarling. There is no doubt he thought he was chasing the intruder away from the village because, having been barked and growled at in a ferocious manner, the plane did escape over the moors to leave the village in peace. There is no doubt that Bushy saw himself as the guardian of Aidensfield.

In his self-imposed role of protector, he could hear the distant approach of the aircraft long before we could, and long before it appeared, and so he prepared himself for the chase by standing in the village street at Aidensfield, bushy tail and sharp ears erect, eyes to the skies and nose pointing towards the oncoming noise. And as the plane flew overhead, Bushy would bark at it and chase it away. He never failed to rid us of a trespassing aircraft – every one of them fled from his strong teeth and loud barking.

The snag was, of course, that aeroplanes did not follow the routes of roads or footpaths. Unlike motor vehicle chasers, Bushy did not confine himself to accepted highways but tore across gardens, through farmyards and over hedges in his efforts to save Aidensfield from aeroplanes.

He demolished several cloches, ruined umpteen newly planted seedbeds, damaged crops of outdoor tomatoes, potatoes, peas, beans and carrots, knocked over pedal cycles, ladders and tins of paint and sent old ladies' shopping baskets flying. Most of the offended humans did not appreciate his gallant efforts to prevent aircraft landing in Aidensfield and so I began to receive complaints about his activities.

I went to see his owner, Mrs Cecily Carter, and told her of the complaints.

'I have written to the RAF,' she said coyly. 'I've asked them not to direct flights over the village but they said they could not divert their flight paths because of a dog. I wrote to the Minister of Aviation too, and he said the same.'

'That's understandable,' I said. 'But if Bushy continues to cause damage in his pursuit of aeroplanes, you're going to receive some hefty bills for compensation or repairs. And, worse still, he could cause an accident to a cyclist or a driver of any kind. He has no road sense when he's chasing his planes away.'

'I really don't know what to do, Mr Rhea, I have had complaints already, he knocked a bucket of whitewash all over someone's front step one day, and another time caused a cyclist to swerve and fall off his bike into a manure heap.'

She recounted several hilarious tales of Bushy's activities and it seems he disliked jets more than planes with propellers. But we had to halt his recklessness.

'What about one of those long leads?' I suggested. 'You might have seen them – they are two posts with a line between them, rather like a clothes-line, and the dog's lead runs along that line. The longer the gap between the posts, the more running space the dog has. If Bushy was given that kind of freedom, he could still chase his planes without causing much havoc. He'd be limited in his gallops and he'd still be happy that he was saving the village from attack.'

And so the deed was done. Bushy had a new run in Mrs Carter's back garden and spent his days protecting us all from advancing aircraft. He did a wonderful job – not one plane has ever landed in Aidensfield.

Some of us wondered what he would have done if one had landed.

Claude Jeremiah Greengrass caused a minor panic when he decided to kill and clean his own pig. In some rural areas, cottagers continued to rear and kill their own pigs, a relic of earlier times, and if there was a spot of easy cash to be made in this way, then Claude Jeremiah would adopt the system. And so he did.

One offshoot of killing and curing one's own pig was the bladder – farm lads would blow up the bladder and use it as a football, and having seen this, Claude decided that the best way to clean the hairs off his dead pig was to inflate it.

He reasoned that if he inflated the pig so that its belly and body were firm and rounded, he could then clean off the surplus hair in a very swift and easy manner. Shaving a man's cheek when it was puffed out with wind was far easier than attempting to clean a sunken cheek. That was his logic.

Having killed the unfortunate animal, therefore, Claude set about sealing all its natural openings and then decided to inflate it. In the corner of one of his outbuildings he had a cylinder of gas; he wasn't quite sure what sort of gas was contained therein but he reckoned it would be perfect for inflating the pig. Later, we thought it might have been propane but no one was quite sure. However, having connected the hose to a suitable place on the pig's anatomy, he proceeded to open the nozzle on the cylinder and allow the escaping gas to change the pig into a very rounded carcass.

Once it was tightly blown up, Claude detached the gas pipe and was about to begin shaving the pig's skin with a cut-throat razor, when he spotted a blowlamp in the shed. Why not singe off the hairs as all good butchers did?

According to his account of events, he lit the blowlamp and

began to apply its flame to the body of the porker, very efficiently removing all the surplus hairs. But suddenly there was an almighty explosion. Claude Jeremiah was enveloped by pieces of flying pig and the noise alerted a neighbour who was hoeing in a nearby field.

He rang the fire brigade because he saw a cloud of smoke emerging from the outbuilding rapidly followed by Claude Jeremiah who was covered in some indescribable mess. The fire brigade was not needed and Claude survived, but the experience put him off smoked bacon for a long, long time. We wrote off the fire call as 'false alarm with good intent' and a senior fire officer warned Claude about using canisters containing unknown fluids and gases.

But another dead animal found in Claude's possession caused a minor flap. A special constable had been coming home from the pub one evening when he noticed Claude's old van leaving the grounds of Lord Ashfordly's estate with a dead stag on the roof. It had a fine set of antlers and seemed in prime condition, according to the witness.

Suspecting a poaching expedition, the special had telephoned Eltering police office and I received a radio call to proceed immediately to the scene. As I was on patrol at the time, it was easy to divert to Ashfordly, but as I reached the road in question, there was no sign of my quarry. This was not surprising as he'd had a few minutes start but, being aware that the special would be well acquainted with Claude, I set off towards his home and arrived in time to see his battered old van being unloaded. Sure enough, as my headlights illuminated the scene, he was lifting the carcass of a deer from his roof-rack.

'Now then, Claude,' I said, going towards him. 'It looks as though we've got you red-handed this time.'

'Red-handed, Mr Rhea? What for?' He looked at me in amazement.

'Poaching,' I said. 'Deer poaching in fact. From Lord Ashfordly's estate . . . you were seen leaving and I have found you in possession of a dead stag, a fallow deer by the look of it. so, what's your story about this one?'

He burst out laughing.

'Nay, lad,' he said. 'This is dead all right, but it's been dead a long time. It's stuffed. Ashfordly threw it out and said I could have it if I would take it away. See, it's moth-eaten and worn out, but I'll sell it somewhere . . . you can't have me for poaching stuffed deer, Mr Rhea. Can you?'

'No,' I said. 'Sorry about this . . . .'

'No problem, Mr Rhea, you're only doing your job,' he chuckled as I crept away. He'd live on that story for years!

A similar incident happened during the summer after the village schoolchildren had been taken on an outing to the zoo. Some of my own youngsters went along and so did the little lad whose parents lived in a cottage close to the police house in Aidensfield. He was called Simon Westhouse and he was six.

Gillian Westhouse was friendly with Mary and asked if Simon could join our children for the trip; Mary wasn't going for the teachers were looking after all the children.

But Gillian had to visit the optician in York that very day and would not return until 5 p.m. So Mary said that, after the trip, Simon could come to our house to play with our children until she returned.

When Elizabeth came home without Simon, Mary asked, 'Where's Simon?'

'He fell in the pond, he's gone straight home to get changed,' she said. 'His shoes and trousers are wet. He knows where the key is, it's under a brick outside the back door.'

'Fell in?' Mary was horrified.

'Only a little.' Elizabeth was not in the least concerned. 'He got his socks wet, that's all. Teacher said to get changed the minute he got home and have a bath before he caught cold.'

Mary went round to the Westhouse cottage and found the door open. She called upstairs to ask if Simon was all right and he shouted that he was.

'I'm getting my wet things off,' he said.

'Come round when you've finished then,' Mary called upstairs to him. 'And have some tea with us.'

But Mrs Westhouse returned home early; Mary had just come back from speaking to Simon when Gillian came to our front door, saying she'd met a friend and had got a lift home. Mary explained about Simon, at which Gillian rushed to attend to him.

But within minutes, she was back at our front door looking worried.

'Nick,' she said. 'Can you come? Simon's locked himself in the bathroom he says he's got a friend with him, he won't let me in.'

'A friend?' I puzzled.

'He was alone when he came home,' said Elizabeth who was hovering nearby. 'Definitely, no one came with him.'

'I'm sure he was talking to someone, I could hear him chattering in the bathroom . . . .'

As Simon was an only child, and as his father was working in York until about eight o'clock, I could understand Gillian's concern. There had been a recent case where a man had entered a child's bedroom to assault the youngster in bed, and it had created a lot of publicity and alarm. So I went around to the house.

As I tapped on the bathroom door, I could hear water splashing in the bath; I repeated my knock and heard Simon saying, 'Don't make a noise, you are my friend. I will look after you . . . .'

'He's got somebody in there,' I said. 'A friend . . . Simon!' I called. 'It's Mr Rhea, can you let me in?'

There was no response.

'Have you a ladder?' I asked Gillian. 'And is the bathroom window open?'

'Yes,' she answered to both questions.

I went outside, placed the ladder against the wall and climbed up to the bathroom window.

It was ajar, and it was an easy task to remove the catch and open it wide. And as I peered inside, I saw Simon sitting in the bath, quite naked, and he was washing a duck.

'Simon!' I called. 'Where on earth did you get that duck?'

'He's my new friend,' he said. 'I brought him home from the zoo . . . .'

It seemed that Simon had taken a fancy to the duck, which was a very tame ornamental specimen, known as a bufflehead. It was a beautiful duck, chiefly white, with black wings and a large black head with purple, blue and green highlights. There was a large white patch on the back of its head. The bird, which is quite a rare species in this country, was just over a foot in length.

Simon had waded into the pond, picked up the bird and stuffed it inside his windcheater. In the darkness of his clothing, the bird had never struggled or cried out and he had brought it home literally under the eye of his teacher. His clothes were wet and dirty but neither he nor the bird was harmed.

'We'll have to take him back,' I said. 'He needs proper food and we have none here, besides he's not yours . . . .'

The zoo officials were very nice about it; in fact, they hadn't noticed the duck's absence and said that Simon could adopt it, although he must leave it at the zoo. And so Simon found himself the adopted father of a bufflehead duck.

He called it Meredith for reasons I shall never know and paid periodic visits to feed and talk to his new friend.

But after their initial meeting, they never again bathed together.

9 Say That Again?

Egad! I think the interpreter is the hardest
to be understood of the two!
Richard Brinsley Sheridan (1751–1816)

The English are noted for their failure to learn the languages
of others. We travel the globe to find that our language is both
spoken and understood by a huge proportion of the world's
population, and consequently we do not trouble to master the
tongues even of our continental neighbours.

Even more astonishing is that we do not truly master our
own language; the grammar of many English people is awful
and one of my pet hates is the wide and annoying use of the
double negative. Quite educated people will say 'I don't want
none of that' or 'I haven't got no more money' or 'I don't want
no more to drink.' Perhaps I am fortunate in having a good
primary school teacher who made sure her pupils did not fall
into that lazy way of speech – she made sure that we
understood that if we hadn't got nothing, it meant we must
have something!

Here in Yorkshire, of course, we are bilingual. We proudly
speak the so-called Queen's English, albeit with a distinctive
accent, but many of us also speak Yorkshire dialect. Dialect is
not mere accent, however. Dialect is the use of ancient and
very local words and phrases.

I have highlighted this aspect of Yorkshire life in earlier
'Constable' books, mentioning that in Yorkshire there are well
over 100 dialects. The language of the West Riding differs
immensely from that of the North Riding which in turn can be
distinguished from that of the East Riding. In North

Yorkshire alone there is a huge difference between the speech of the dales and the speech of the coastline. Perhaps it takes a keen ear to distinguish such differences, but I thought I would include a handful of words now, just to show that Yorkshire folk do speak a different language and do not merely speak with a distinctive accent.

Here are a few dialect words: bautering, betwaddled, bounderstoops, brummelneeased, canthrif, caumbrils, chalter-heeaded, clocker, crambazzled, gallowers, gammerstang, glishy, goulders, grouty, jaggins, jotherum, ket, lagged, loppered, parlous, parsling, reeafshafts, rudsteeaks, scalderings, scran, semmanty, shackles, sieves, skelbeeasts, skimmer, spawldering, swingletrees, theeaking, tivvying, yamley and yows. There are thousands of such words which pepper the conversation of country folk, particularly those in the more remote parts of the Yorkshire Dales and the North York Moors.

Many older folk do not know any other word for the object in question, consequently there are bound to be misunderstandings. On the moors near my home, a visitor asked the purpose of a small enclosure and the farmer said, 'Whey, it's where t'yowes are heeafed.'

A yow is a ewe, the moorland sheep roaming free upon our moors, but the youngsters remain enclosed with their mums until they know their unmarked boundaries. When released, they will then remain upon that stretch of moorland without being fenced in. Heeaf is the local word for that procedure; heaf or heeaf means abode or habitat. Ewes that are heeafed are those which know their boundaries. My moorland friend explained that in a handful of words, but his listener still failed to understand.

Fortunately, I was brought up to speak my native North Riding dialect and consequently had no trouble understanding the conversations of true Yorkshire folk, but even so many misunderstandings did arise.

For example, a lady motorist stopped in Aidensfield to seek directions from me. She asked if there was a bank in the village, so I sent her along to the outskirts where a steep hill climbs to the moors. I thought she wanted to park the car somewhere with wide open views of the countryside, and there was a lovely position at the top of that bank. She returned and said she could not find the bank – all she had found was a very steep hill with moorland around it. In Yorkshire, a bank is a steep hill – it seems she was seeking a place to draw out some cash.

A clear case of misunderstanding which could have had fatal consequences occurred in the West Riding, a county with its own distinctive mode of speech.

When British Rail installed its early automatic level-crossing barriers, there were advance warnings upon our roads in the form of flashing lights and large written signs.

The signs told motorists to 'Stop while lights flash'. Those of us outside the West Riding, which includes the rest of the world, would have halted our vehicles and waited when the lights were flashing because that flashing indicated the coming of a train. But in the West Riding, 'while' means 'until'. A West Yorkshire person will say 'wait while I return' which in their case means 'wait until I return'. Thus, when our friends from West Yorkshire first encountered those new signs, they halted their cars to wait *until* the lights flashed – and then set off! For them, the sign's message was exactly the opposite of that which was intended. The confusion was quickly rectified with no fatalities. Now, the signs clearly tell us to stop when the lights show.

During my service at Aidensfield, I did encounter some minor embarrassments because of my Yorkshire manner of speech. One which bears repeating occurred at a garden fête where the lady of the manor asked me to instruct one of her members of staff to fetch the white Jag. I found him and said that her ladyship wanted the white Jaguar, whereupon he said they didn't have a white Jaguar. It transpired she wanted a drink of orange squash which was in a white jug on one of the stalls. She'd asked for the white jug, not the white Jag.

Here in Yorkshire, a jug is jug, not a jag; a bus is a bus and not a bass, grass is grass and not grarse, bath is bath and not barth, and we also pronouce 'fat' correctly.

Similarly, when it was suggested that Lady Ashfordly be asked to open a garden fête and remain as guest of honour, the posh-speaking secretary of the organizers, at whose meeting I was present, made it clear that three chairs would have to be arranged for her. I could not understand why she needed three chairs, unless she was bringing friends, and the same puzzle baffled the chairman.

'What's she want three chairs for?' he asked the secretary.

'Cheers, you silly man,' she said. 'Hip, hip, hoorays. Cheers, not chairs. We need to arrange three cheers for her ladyship after her opening speech.'

It was this kind of misunderstanding that caused something of a flap due to some visiting, trouble-seeking students overhearing a discussion about a lorry accident.

A loaded lorry ran away down the hill leading into Aidensfield. Its driver managed to steer it off the road and it ran on to the moor but continued several yards down a slope and overturned into a gully, spilling its load. The driver was not injured and managed to climb out of the passenger side window to seek assistance. The lorry was carrying five tons of gravel; this spilt into a narrow gully which, in winter, was the course of a fast-running moorland stream.

In summer, the time of the accident, the gully was dry but the local people knew that the heap of gravel must be cleared away as soon as possible; if there was a thunder-storm or a cloudburst, floodwater from the moors would normally flow safely down that gully and into the river, but if the water's route was blocked, it would overflow on to the road and could cause flood damage to houses and farm buildings. The heap of gravel was causing that kind of blockage and although there was no immediate urgency to remove it, it should be done as soon as possible. The hot, dry conditions could quickly give rise to thunder-storms and sudden heavy rainfall.

In the pub that day, some university students, on an expedition of the surrounding moors to gather information about a future campaign against grouse shooting overheard part of a conversation relating to that accident. They heard only a few words but as they were animal activists of rather a militant frame of mind, they felt they had stumbled upon an awful plot against the animal kingdom and decided to take positive action.

What they heard was a man, who was in fact a member of the county council's highway maintenance section, saying,

'We'll have to get rid o' them chimps as soon as possible. Ah've had words with our gaffer, Ah managed ti catch him just as he was leaving t'zoo after we'd finished that last job, and he reckons they can be left on t'moor overnight. They won't be in anybody's way up there but we'll have to get rid of 'em as soon as we can. There'll be trouble if they're left there.'

His pal had said, 'We could allus chuck some of 'em down t'cliff into that awd quarry, that'd get rid o' some.'

'We can't leave 'em blocking that gully; a pile o' chimps in that spot'll send t'flood watter down inti Aidensfield.'

'We could allus flatten some wi' shovels and spades,' said another.

'We'll need a wagon handy ti cart 'em off,' was another suggestion. 'They're quite heavy, too heavy and too many to shift by hand. Mebbe we should fetch an excavator?'

What the students did not know was that 'chimps' is a local word for pieces of gravel. When small piles of gravel are placed at intervals along the verges for use on the roads in winter conditions, we always call them 'chimp heaps'. Chimpings is an old word which, I believe, originally meant husked, unground oats, these pieces also being known as grits. In recent years, however, chimps has come to be used to describe small pieces of gravel or road grit. For the people of the moors a pile of chimps means a pile of gravel or grit.

Those students, however, in eavesdropping upon part of that conversation, assumed that the men were going to secretly and cruelly dispose of some chimpanzees which lived in the local zoo. They thought the men were part of a conspiracy to kill the chimps by battering them with shovels and spades; the men would carry their bodies on to the moors in a lorry, and then get rid of them by throwing the corpses into a quarry. It had the elements of a fiendish plot by uncaring country folk.

The students decided to halt the slaughter; they would create publicity for their new-found cause by organizing a protest at the gates of the zoo. It was with some surprise, therefore, that early the following morning the proprietor of the zoo found two dozen students outside his front entrance, all waving banners saying 'Save the Chimps'.

Mr Lawrence went out to talk to them with the intention of finding the reason for their presence.

'We want to stop the slaughter of the chimpanzees,' said the student leader.

'What chimpanzees?' asked the puzzled Mr Lawrence.

'Your chimpanzees. We've overheard a plot to kill them by inhumane methods, and to dispose of their bodies on the moor,' was the answer. 'It smacks of Fascism and capitalist cruelty.'

'You must be joking!' he laughed. 'Now look, there is no such plan, I assure you. Our chimps are healthy and well cared for; we have no plans to dispose of any of them and if one is ill, we always secure the services of a vet. We've never had to kill one, and have no such intentions. If we did want to get rid of any of our animals, it would always be done with compassion and by experts.'

'That's exactly what you would say,' shouted one of the protesters. 'It's a cover-up, we've heard the plotters . . . we have called the press and we intend to draw the attention of the public to this gross act of Fascist cruelty to animals and to the uncaring attitudes of capitalist zoo-keepers . . . .'

'I have no idea what you are talking about,' responded Mr Lawrence. But after speaking to the protesters for several minutes without convincing them of his innocence, he rang Sergeant Blaketon. Blaketon rang me.

'Rhea,' he said. 'I'll pick you up in quarter of an hour. We're going to the zoo.'

'That'll be nice,' I joked. 'I could do with a day out.'

'Don't be facetious, Rhea. It's work. There's a protest of some kind. Lefty students waving banners and shouting slogans.'

I groaned. At that time, left-wing students and their rent-a-mob pals were protesting about almost everything and as we drove to the zoo, Sergeant Blaketon explained our mission.

'They are blocking the road, Rhea, they've congregated

outside the main entrance but have the sense not to trespass inside. They're asking visitors to join them in their protest. The press has been called by the student leader too, so we'll have to tread warily. We don't want our pictures in the papers; you know how some students throw red paint over themselves to make it appear we've clobbered them, or spread marbles on the road to make it impossible for police horses to stand upright.'

'Have the mounted section been called out?' I asked with some surprise.

'No, they have not. I'm just warning you about the dirty tricks some left-wingers play to gain public sympathy.'

'What are they protesting about?' I asked. 'Did Mr Lawrence give you any idea?'

'Something about slaughtering monkeys,' said Sergeant Blaketon. 'They're objecting to that.'

'Is the zoo slaughtering monkeys?' I asked.

'How should I know what they do with their old monkeys?' Blaketon shrugged his shoulders and we drove on. When we arrived, we were greeted by catcalls and jeers from the scruffy bunch of layabouts which had gathered at the entrance, but Blaketon ignored them as we drove into the zoo and parked before the office block. Mr Lawrence came out to meet us.

'Thanks for coming,' he said. 'That lot's upsetting our visitors. I've had the press on to me as well, about slaughtering chimpanzees by inhumane methods. Sergeant, I've no idea what they are talking about or who sent them here.'

'You do have monkeys here?' asked Blaketon.

'Yes, a wide variety of them, all well cared for. It's chimps they're talking about, they saw they overheard a plot to kill our chimps and dispose of their carcasses on the moors.'

'And you have no such plans?' asked Blaketon.

'No, of course not. If we do have to dispose of any of our sick or dead animals, we would never dump their bodies on the moors anyway. That lot out there are puddled, Sergeant; God knows what rumours they've heard.'

'Show me your chimps, Mr Lawrence,' said Blaketon. 'And Rhea, you go and have a word with the student leader. Find out just what he has heard and why he's brought this scruffy mob here.'

I walked out of the main gate and called for the leader to come to me. His companions were shouting abuse at my uniform but a small, bearded youth with granny specs and ten days' growth of unwashed dirt about his face and clothes, now stepped forward with a swagger.

'You're on his side, mate,' he spat on the ground. 'You'll make us clear off and those animals will die . . . .'

'I want you to tell me what you heard,' I said quietly, ignoring their behaviour.

A girl said, 'They're going to get rid of the chimps . . . .'

Another butted in, 'And dump them down a quarry after flattening them with spades and shovels . . .'

'And leave them on the moor all night, then get a wagon to cart them away . . . .'

'Where did you hear this?' I asked.

'In the pub at Aidensfield,' said the leader. 'Last night, a bunch of Fascists talking about it, we overheard them.'

'And they were talking about getting rid of the chimps?' I asked, having now gained their attention.

'Yep, they were. One of the men had been to the zoo . . . .'

As they outlined their version of the conversation they'd overheard, I thought quickly. Now I knew what they were talking about, I knew about the pile of chimps in the gully and the worries about moving them, because I had dealt with the lorry accident. And I also reckoned these protesters needed to be taught a gentle lesson.

'I know where you mean,' I said. 'I saw the chimps there myself, but they're not from this zoo.'

'Not from this zoo? Then where are they from? And what are you doing about it then?' The words came from a smelly face which leered into mine. 'Bloody capitalists, making capital out of captive animals, getting rid of them in this cruel manner when they've earned filthy money to line their pockets . . . .'

'I've made a report, they're coming to move them today,' I said, looking at my watch. 'About now, in fact. Now, I'm a believer in kindness to dumb animals, so if you like, I could take you there . . . .'

'With the press?' The leader did not entirely trust me.

'With the press,' I agreed. 'They can come too. But I must first have words with my sergeant and Mr Lawrence. And I reckon you owe an apology to Mr Lawrence. You've picked the wrong target this time, lads.'

At that moment, Sergeant Blaketon reappeared and called the leader to him. 'I have inspected the chimpanzees and they are all present and in good health,' he said. 'If you, the leader that is, would care to accompany me, I will show you the chimpanzees, with the approval of Mr Lawrence. You can inspect them yourself, you don't have to take my word.'

The leader looked at me and shook his head. 'No, no need, not now. We want to go with the constable to see the ones that we really ought to be looking at. It's not those at this zoo.'

Sergeant Blaketon looked at me. 'What's all this, Constable Rhea?'

'These people have made a mistake, Sergeant, and they accept it. The chimps they are protesting about are out on the moors above Aidensfield, they're there now, I saw them myself.'

'You did? Where, Rhea?' The expression on Sergeant Blaketon's face was a joy to behold and none of the protesters missed it. His reaction confirmed my story and I had them on my side now, they trusted me.

'I've promised to show these people the place and the chimps, Sergeant. Most of the chimps will still be there, council workmen are planning to move them this morning.'

'Why didn't I know about this?' bellowed Blaketon.

'It was your day off yesterday,' I reminded him. 'Perhaps you hadn't time to read the Occurrence Book before you were called out here?'

'Rhea, I don't know what's going on but . . . .'

'Trust me, Sergeant,' I hoped he wasn't going to make a mess of my plot. 'I think this gentleman wishes to apologize to Mr Lawrence, and when he's done so, I shall be happy to guide him and his friends to the site on the moors. It is only fair, after all, these people have made a legitimate protest but at the wrong place, and I can only be fair to them by showing them the chimps in question. These are the chimps referred to in the pub last night. What action they take is then up to them, so long as it is lawful. And I'll show the press too.'

'I don't know what you're up to, Rhea, but I'll need a full report of this when it's all over!'

The students cheered at him and I smiled at them conspiratorially.

'Yes, Sergeant,' I concurred.

Minutes later, watched by a puzzled Mr Lawrence, we prepared to drive off in convoy. I called to him, 'I'll ring you later Mr Lawrence, to explain things.'

The convoy of scruffy old vans and scooters, with two press cars in attendance, then followed us from the zoo. As Blaketon drove along, he was silent and then he said,

'We're going to look real fools over this, Rhea, you showing this mob some chimps that have been dumped on the moor. It'll only make them protest more . . . where the hell have those chimps come from? And who dumped them on our moorland?'

'They're from an accident involving a lorry,' I explained. 'Chimps is our local word for gravel, Sergeant. I'm going to show them a pile of gravel that's being cleared away right now. And I'm going to get the press to take a picture of them looking at chimps but looking like chumps.'

'You mean they got it all wrong?' he chuckled.

'Yes,' I said. 'They overheard some chaps in the pub and got the wrong end of the stick. It serves them right for eavesdropping and for interfering in the business of others. Now we can teach them a lesson.'

'I'm going to enjoy this,' smiled Oscar Blaketon.

But when we arrived at the scene of the crash, the damaged lorry had been removed with heavy lifting gear, and a replacement had been manoeuvred into the gully so that it was in position to be loaded with the gravel. Then things took another startling turn.

The highway department's lorry was parked with a plank leading from its rear down to the ground at the base of the huge pile of gravel and several wheelbarrows and shovels stood by. The council workmen, three of them, were sitting in a canvas hut on the moor having their mid-morning break. As

Blaketon and I eased to a halt, the convoy of battered vehicles and scruffy protesters pulled up.

'Down there!' I waited until everyone had joined me, including the press reporters and photographers, then pointed to the heap of chimps in the gully. 'The chimps are down there. I'm going to have words with the foreman first!'

My intention was to explain the course of events to him and to let the press take their pictures as I explained that the pile of gravel was the 'chimps' about which they were protesting, but as I walked across to the canvas hut, I heard the leader shout,

'You mean down there? Under that pile of grit?'

'Yes,' I said. 'I'll explain in a minute . . . .'

'Right lads,' said the leader. 'Grab some shovels, shovel all that grit back into that bloody wagon! They've buried the bodies under this pile of grit . . . the bastards . . . .'

'Rhea,' said Sergeant Blaketon. 'They've going to shovel that grit away . . . .'

'Which is exactly what we want, Sergeant, isn't it?'

When I told the foreman what was happening, he chuckled and said his men could have a longer break with more time to play cards, while the volunteers shovelled away the huge pile of gravel. I had words with the journalists who were standing aside and suggested they take pictures of the action.

'I want to see them uncover the chimps,' said one photographer.

'That's just what they're doing. In this part of Yorkshire, chimps means gravel. That is a pile of chimps, that's what these idiots are protesting about – we were going to get rid of this pile of chimps, not kill chimpanzees in the zoo.'

'Really?' beamed the photographer who then told his colleagues, and so they secured some excellent shots of the protesters shovelling away the pile of gravel. As the energetic shovelling reached the bottom of the heap, it was gratifying to see the wagon fully loaded; as the foreman, beaming at his good fortune, secured the tailboard, the leader came across to me and Sergeant Blaketon.

'There's no sign of any chimps,' he was angry now and sweating profusely from his actions, 'Are you sure they were buried here?'

'Absolutely,' beamed Sergeant Blaketon. 'Five tons of 'em. You've done right well for the highways department by shifting those chimps.'

'I've not seen any chimps,' he said, frowning.

'Between you, you've shovelled the best part of five tons of them,' I laughed. 'Perhaps it will teach you a lesson about good behaviour – and a lesson in local language. The chimps that were going to be got rid of are those – the gravel. Chimps is our local word for gravel . . . the few bits you've left will be thrown down the quarry, as you overheard, or washed away by the next heavy rainfall.'

'You bastards . . .' he cursed. 'You've taken us for a ride . . . .'

The press men were rapidly taking pictures of the departing council wagon, into which someone had stuck one of the banners. The lorry departed with the slogan 'Save Our Chimps' waving from the heap of gravel in the rear.

The photographers hurried off with their pictures and I wondered what the rabble would do. Would they become violent? But they turned their anger towards their leader and began to curse him as they all trooped back to their old vehicles and scooters before disappearing over the horizon.

Later that week, the local paper had a lovely photograph of them removing the pile of gravel beneath the slogan, MONKEY BUSINESS AMONG THE CHIMPS.

Mr Lawrence was delighted when I told him the story and I learned that the publicity had also helped the zoo. The highways department enjoyed it too – they sent a gift of a load of chimps to be spread upon the path outside the chimpanzee enclosure.

Misunderstandings of a more elementary type also occur, often through one party misinterpreting the instructions of another. There are lots of humorous examples, such as the question from a rail passenger who asks, 'How long will the next train be?' whereupon the porter answers, 'An engine and five coaches.' There are many examples where people have placed a precise meaning upon the words of others and Mary, my wife, encountered an example when she was working in

Brantsford Orthopaedic Hospital.

She was helping in the wing that specialized in old folks' problems when a new auxiliary nurse arrived. She would be about seventeen and was anxious to make herself useful.

Mary was busy with the old folks, perhaps too busy to give the nurse the guidance or help that she needed, but the youngster asked,

'Is there anything I can do?'

Mary thought fast. 'Yes, there is, Sandra,' she said. 'You can clean the old folks' teeth.'

'Right,' said the girl, full of enthusiasm.

But Mary was too occupied to supervise the girl as she went about her task. Unknown to Mary, Sandra had visited every one of the old folks in the various wards, about twenty-five in total, and had extracted their false teeth. These she had placed in a bucket which she had then taken to a washroom; she had then set about scrubbing all the teeth with a nail-brush.

When Mary went into the room, she found Sandra with the bucket and the sets of cleaned teeth grinning from the draining-board. Those awaiting attention were still in the bucket, like a lot of grinning pink lobsters.

'What's happening, Sandra?' Mary asked.

'I'm cleaning the old folks' teeth, like you said,' was the innocent response.

'And how do you know which teeth belong to which person?' smiled Mary.

The expression on the girl's face said everything. Sandra hadn't a clue where to replace each of the sets of gnashers but Mary thought she should learn a lesson. She made Sandra take the cleaned teeth back to the wards to try to find the owners. Some of the patients might recognize their own, but many would not and so the task would be one of trial and error, of fitting and testing, of chewing and whistling.

It took ages. But when Sandra had finished, and when the old folks were wondering why their teeth weren't quite so comfortable as they had been, Sandra had a set left over.

'I've got a set left, Mrs Rhea.' She looked bewildered. 'I'm so sorry . . . I just didn't think.'

'Have they all got a set of teeth?' Mary asked.

'Yes, I've been round them all again and again, they've all got teeth in.'

At that moment, Dr Brownlee, the consultant, came into the ward. 'Mary,' he called to my wife. 'Do a check will you? Somebody's removed a set of dentures from the corpse in the mortuary. We're doing an inventory of his personal belongings. See if you can find them, will you?'

'Sandra?' called Mary.

10 Out of the Frying Pan and into the Fire

Kindled a flame I still deplore
(Words from a riddle in
Lady's Magazine, *June 1762)*

Throughout history, there have been people whose activities upon this earth have left overwhelming disaster in their wake – we can mention modern ones such as Hitler, Stalin, Lenin and Robert Maxwell as well as umpteen socialist heads of state and would-be financial wizards. Lower down the scale there have been several incompetent do-it-yourself fanatics of personal acquaintance whose efforts to repair houses have succeeded only in damaging them, and others of lesser fame such as the holidaymaker on a canal boat who left open the lock-gates which caused the escaping waters to flood a village, and those who leave cars parked on hills without setting the hand-brake.

The activities of some disaster-merchants rarely reach the headlines, however, and I'm sure that some do sincerely try to do well in their span on this earth – it's just that they fail in their grandiose plans and leave others to pick up the proverbial pieces or clean up the resultant mess. Many try only to please themselves as they pursue a selfish life of leisure and financial trickery and leave behind a trail of suffering victims. In some cases, the police become aware of the problems thus created.

John George Crossfield was such a disaster-merchant. I had never met him until I came across him late one afternoon on the moors above Aidensfield, and it is the background circumstances of that meeting that I shall now relate. I learned of his past activities after my first meeting with him – his life and crimes were well documented in the files of several police forces.

John George was a womanizer of considerable talent. Smooth-tongued, well-dressed, with expensive tastes and a flair for showmanship, he could charm the pants off any lady with his stories of life in exotic places, his relationships with famous people and the massive wealth he had at his disposal. But it was all talk – he had no wealth, he did not even own a house or a car and lived expensively on borrowed money which was never repaid. He 'bought' cars without ever paying for them, he lived in expensive hotels and left without paying his bills, he charmed money out of gullible women with whom he went on holiday under the pretext of marrying them upon their return and he tried several times to start businesses, all of which failed miserably after incurring colossal debts. But he had what is known as a silver tongue and could talk his way out of most predicaments. There were times, it seemed, that he actually believed his own claims.

From the viewpoint of his lady victims, there is no doubt he was handsome in appearance and a worthy companion at socially acceptable events.

In his late thirties, John George kept himself very fit by lots of exercise and he maintained his good looks by persuading rich ladies to accompany him (and to pay for him) on regular trips to the Mediterranean where he acquired fine tans and expensive clothes at their expense.

Not quite six feet tall, he was well-built with an athletic body and had a splendid head of beautifully groomed jet-black hair, splendid white teeth and velvety dark brown eyes which could charm a woman off her bar stool in a matter of seconds. When God had issued good looks, John George must have been first in the queue. He had the lithe form of a Spanish matador, but the morals of a tom-cat and the expensive tastes of an Arabian sheikh.

John George drove fast cars (which he never paid for) and even claimed to have a yacht moored near Southampton which he used for cruising around the Greek islands. We were to learn that he had 'hired' the yacht from a very wealthy friend who had fallen for his charms and believed his stories. He had followed this life style for many years, usually avoiding prosecution for fraud because none of his lady companions wished to make a formal complaint. Some even paid off his debts but his method of thanking them was to leave them alone as he concentrated upon yet another female conquest or dubious business deal.

Then he met Yvonne Patricia Carlton-Kinross, a lady of aristocratic background with financial interests in several Texan oil wells and property on Manhattan Island, New York. She was tall and lithe, a honey blonde in her early thirties with an exquisite figure and a penchant for fast cars and expensive jewels. She was, in fact, a qualified doctor who travelled the world lecturing on feminine medical problems. It was while staying at one of Harrogate's finest hotels that she encountered John George who, after buying her an expensive cocktail at the bar, promptly launched into his lady-killing playboy routine. He displayed his gold-plated cigarette-case, his expensive cuff-links and said he had just come home after concluding a successful business deal in Sydney, Australia, hinting that he had bought a top Australian newspaper group.

But Yvonne was oblivious to his charm. She studiously ignored all his attempts to woo her, albeit letting him buy her drinks and dinner, and the outcome was that, before the week was out, John George fell hopelessly in love with Yvonne. He had never fallen truly in love before; it was a new experience for him which was aggravated by the fact that Yvonne was not in the least impressed by his bravura or extravagant claims.

The effect was devastating. John George tried to woo her, he tried to get her into bed, he later tried to follow her around the country on her English tour, but she refused to succumb to his considerable charm. She agreed to be friends, but nothing more.

John George worked very hard upon this new challenge; he bought her meals, he took her to the theatre, he even took her to Ascot, Wimbledon and Henley and, more unusually, he actually paid for all their outings. But as a reward for all his efforts, he received nothing more than a polite 'thank you', some light praise for giving her a lovely outing, followed by a tiny peck on the cheek.

At long last, it seemed, John George had met his match. Here was a woman whose wealth, charm and overwhelming beauty was finer than anything he had ever encountered, and yet here was one who utterly refused to be swayed by his pretentious claims. In truth, her own background was far more glittering than anything he could conjure from his imagination. She had the style, whereas, he had to admit, he had nothing but the figments of his own imagination.

Finally, on her last night in England, he did receive an invitation to her suite at a splendid hotel in Bristol. Full of joy and romantic vision, he rushed off to buy two dozen red roses and a bottle of champagne, and duly presented himself at Room 109. Here was a promise of bliss. In the happy but preliminary moments that followed, and with the promise of yet more happiness before she left for America, Yvonne had explored his body with her sensitive hands and had then reacted with shock.

'John George!' she had shrieked. 'You'll have to see a specialist . . . .'

'Why?' he had spluttered.

'Your heart . . . it sounds terrible, irregular, fighting to push your blood around . . . you must never strain yourself again . . . I'm a doctor, remember; look, I've got a good friend in Harley Street. I'll make an appointment . . . .'

And so the night from which he had expected so much had ended in disaster. John George Crossfield found himself taking a taxi across London to an address in Harley Street where a pompous specialist had pronounced that John George, at the early age of thirty-six, appeared to have prematurely hardening arteries with more than a hint of something amiss with his liver. A lifespan of no more than six months awaited those with such an advanced form of arteriosclerosis and in addition, cancer of the liver or cancer of some other internal organ was hinted at. A further appointment was made at great expense for John George, and so he found himself being prodded and poked by another doctor in Hull who said he ought to be admitted to hospital for a barium meal followed by a rigorous examination by a cancer specialist. The doctor would write to John George the moment a vacancy occurred.

All these dramas occurred within days of the departure of Yvonne to the States; she had certainly made things happen for his welfare, and all these tests and worries were crowded into the life of John George Crossfield before he arrived on the North York Moors above Aidensfield.

As he was undergoing his various tests and medical examinations, there is little doubt he felt very much alone and very vulnerable. Dr Yvonne had returned to America but before leaving, had promised she would keep in touch. And she was as good as her word. As he waited for a date for his barium meal, he received a telegram from the USA it was signed by Yvonne and it said she would not be returning to England. She had decided to settle in America because she had been offered a teaching post at a famous medical university and, besides, she had had an offer of marriage from a professor of obstetrics. John George was devastated. With death imminent and the threat of cancer hovering as an additional death-warrant, and with his only true lady-love deserting him, John George decided to end it all. He would commit suicide.

He managed to buy an old Ford Consul from a scrap-yard and motored to the North York Moors, to a place where he had spent an idyllic childhood. It was a pretty place high on the moors above Aidensfield where an uncle had once lived, and now, in the heat of summer, it was perfect. In the boot he had a small green tent with which to hide his shame from the world, and so he arrived at the scene of his demise, pitched his tent on an elevated patch of moorland and prepared his last supper.

As he'd done so many times as a child, he had cooked himself some sausages and bacon over an open fire made with pieces of wood and old stalks of heather, and, having enjoyed his final meal, settled down to die.

To speed him on his way to the happy hereafter, he had taken a large quantity of sleeping tablets; having taken what he thought was sufficient to send him into oblivion, he crept into his tent to shield his dying body from the sight of passers-by, then lay down in his sleeping-bag, zipped it up and waited for the end. He reckoned that if anyone did pass by this lonely place, they would not invade the privacy of the small green tent and so he would be allowed to die in peace and his body would remain upon the moors for a long, long time. As he crept inside, the evening sun was setting in the west.

In fact, John George, had chosen well. The location was a place that few, if any, people would pass during the average course of a year or two. It was remote, it was hidden in the depths of a cleft in the moors and it was well away from all the more popular footpaths. His body might lie there, undiscovered, for years.

But in preparing so well for his departure, John George had forgotten to put out his fire. It was some distance from his tent and as the sticks were reduced to glowing embers, a stiff north-easterly breeze arose while the sun was setting. As John George lay down to pass from this world to the next, so the breeze strengthened and it began to fan the dying embers into tiny flames. Some pieces of burning ash were blown from the fire and settled in the tinder-dry heather and bracken until the inevitable happened. A potentially devastating moor fire was ignited.

The keen breeze fanned the tiny flames into larger ones which, in seconds, gained a hold on the dry grass, heather and bracken and within minutes, a patch of moorland close to John George's tent was ablaze. But the breeze was blowing from behind the tent, carrying the fire away from it; within twenty minutes, the flames were racing through the heather and bracken as they were fanned by the stiffening breeze, and a huge pall of black, grey and white smoke began to gather in the sky.

Had the wind been a westerly, John George would have been roasted alive, but because it was blowing off the sea, his inert body knew nothing of the inferno being created only yards away. But every puff of wind created the blaze further from the silent tent and within half an hour the tent was out of danger but the sky above was filled with thick dark smoke.

A moorland gamekeeper, checking the season's grouse chicks, noticed the pall of smoke over Whinbush Moor and instantly assessed the danger. He hurried to a telephone and raised the alarm, and very soon a host of practised beaters and volunteers, plus the fire brigade from Strensford, turned out to fight the flames. They knew that if the fire burned deep into the peat which carpeted the moors, it would burn for months. The peat is up to thirty feet deep in places, and a fire can smoulder in those depths for months before breaking out again to sweep across the dry moorland. In fighting a moorland fire, speed is vital, but the volunteers knew their job.

Like the others, I received the alarm call and hurried to the location in my mini-van, parking it among the other emergency vehicles in a safe place. I found myself on the southern edge of the fire and, after arming myself with a beater, a long shaft with a flat blade at the end, I began to beat the advancing flames in an attempt to put them out. It was a hot, smelly, perspiring task and as one flame succumbed to my efforts, other tongues would break out as the fire was fanned by the ever present wind. I did not count the numbers who were trying to beat out the flames, but there were hundreds and every one of us knew that we must conquer the blaze because it was relentlessly advancing towards Gelderslack.

That remote moorland village stands literally upon the edge of the moor and if we did not extinguish the fire before it reached the village, it could destroy some of the cottages; indeed, some have thatched roofs and so, as we worked, we prayed that the breeze would drop and that the sultry summer conditions would produce a thunder-storm. A thorough soaking of thundery rain would be a true godsend.

As we tried to beat out the flames, an advance party set off across the moor to dig out a wide barrier of heather by using an earth-moving machine, thus creating a wide band of bare peat between the fire and Gelderslack. Without the surface heather and bracken, the advancing flames would have more difficulty in gaining a hold.

A dry stone wall in the path of the flames was another means of halting its advance but it was impossible to build such a wall in the time available. Likewise, there was no time to demolish any of the local walls with an earth-moving machine and to transport the stones into the path of the flames. As always, the fire brigade, well-trained in dealing with moorland fires, was at the forefront of the battle and, fortunately, able to make use of a moorland stream for its water supply. Five small tenders had managed to gain access to the advancing front and so a fine battle was being fought.

Then I saw one of the volunteers racing through the blackened moorland towards me, gesticulating and shouting. I could not hear his words due to the crackle of flames and the noise of our activity, but hurried towards him. It was Jack Lewis, a farmer from High Garth.

'Mr Rhea, Mr Rhea,' he coughed with the action of the smoke. 'There's a chap in a tent ovver t'brow, out like light, seems ti me t'fire started hard by his tent.'

'Is he dead?' I asked.

'Nay,' he tried to get back his breath. 'He's unconscious, I reckon. He's in a badly way, mind, he needs attention.'

'I'll come,' I said.

And that was when I found John George Crossfield. At that moment, of course, I had no idea who he was or why he had chosen to attempt suicide, but a quick inspection showed me the awful pallor of his skin and his deep, slow breathing.

Closer examination revealed that his pulse was very slow and weak, and I found an empty bottle of sleeping tablets on the floor of his tent.

'Hospital, Jack,' I said. 'Immediately. Barbiturate overdose if I'm not mistaken. Can you help me to carry him to my van?'

Picking up the empty bottle for the hospital's reference, I gave the casualty the fireman's lift across the moor with Jack doing likewise for part of the way and between us we reached my parked van. I hoped that our jerking movements would help keep him alive – one of the first aid treatments in cases of barbiturate overdose is to try to keep the patient awake or even to make them vomit. But this fellow was in a deep stupor although not yet at coma stage.

After plonking the unconscious man in the front passenger seat, I radioed for an ambulance and said I'd meet it on the highroad above Gelderslack, at the junction with the Rannockdale road. I stressed that the casualty looked like someone who had taken a barbiturate overdose and, as Jack went back to fight the fire, I bumped across the moor towards the rendezvous point. The ambulance arrived within quarter of an hour of my arrival, took the casualty and the empty bottle with its informative label, and sped off. I told them I had no idea who the fellow was – I would begin my enquiries once we'd got the blaze under control and would contact Strensford Hospital at the first opportunity.

It took more than four hours of concentrated effort by something like a hundred volunteers and four fire appliances and their crews, to get the fire under control. We were aided by a reduction in the strength of the breeze and, later, around two the following morning, it began to rain. Our prayers had been answered and so we mastered yet another moorland fire; even as we departed, however, the fire brigade retained a presence on the moors until well into the next day, as a precautionary measure. There had been immense damage and it would be impossible to estimate the cost of the damage, both in financial terms and in the devastation to the wildlife.

Young conifers, silver birch and hundreds of gorse bushes had been burned to the ground; acres of heather had been destroyed, as had the nests of countless grouse, skylarks and other ground-nesting birds with their young. Lizards and other mammals had perished, the insect life was devastated and many examples of rare moorland plants had been destroyed. Lots of habitats had disappeared beneath a desert of ash while much of the surface peat had been irreparably damaged.

Once I knew the fire was under control, I walked across to the isolated tent. I saw the remains of the camp-fire and the patch of blackened moorland which surrounded it, and it was easy to follow the path of the fire from that point. I drew the attention of the fire brigade to the remains of the fire, letting them decide whether in fact the devastation had been a direct consequence of this man's camp-fire.

I searched the tent for anything of value, but found nothing apart from the sleeping-bag and later, the old car. I took down the tent and stored it and the bag in my van for eventual return to its owner. Then I went home for a late bath; Mary groaned as I walked into the bedroom for I disturbed her sleep, but even in her own half-wakefulness, she had enough stamina to say that I stank of smoke and smelled as if I'd been working in a bonfire. I got to bed at 4.30 a.m.

I telephoned the hospital at 9 a.m., having caught about four hours sleep, to ask after the gentleman who had attempted suicide. I was told that he'd survived; we had found him in time and his stomach had been pumped to rid him of the residue of the tablets. At that time, in the late 1960s, suicide was no longer a crime. Once, it was a crime known as felo de se (felon of one's self) although it was recognized there could be no earthly punishment. It ceased to be a crime with the passing of the Suicide Act of 1961 and consequently attempted suicide was no longer a crime either. Until that time, attempted suicide had been a crime and it did carry a penalty, although few attempted suicides ever reached a court. Other forms of treatment were considered far more suitable.

That fairly recent change in the law, however, meant that the patient had not committed any criminal offence by his actions but I still had to submit a report about the incident, particularly as his actions seemed to have started a devastating and dangerous moorland fire.

For my report, I had to interview the fellow in hospital and waited until the doctor gave me the necessary permission. It was then that I learned the name of the patient in their care but now he was most contrite, giving me a full account of his exploits and promising to mend his ways, if only for the few months of life that remained. He told me everything about his heart trouble, his supposed cancer of the liver and his ill-fated romance. His happy world had come to a sudden and very abrupt end and so he had decided to conclude his useless life in a place which he had offered everlasting happy memories. I felt touched by his frankness.

'What does the hospital say about your heart condition?' I asked him after we'd had a cup of tea together and after I'd got the necessary information for my report.

'I daren't ask,' he said. 'No, I got the hard word from Harley Street . . . I won't try to end things now, Constable, I'll battle on . . . after all, life is very precious, isn't it?'

'It is,' I said, thinking of those acres of destroyed moorland and the devastated wildlife. 'But surely you've told the doctors here? About the Harley Street verdict, your heart, your forthcoming cancer tests?'

'No,' he said. 'They saved me from myself. I've been a bloody fool, Constable, I'll try to do some good for someone before I do leave this world.'

As there was no question of him having deliberately set fire to the moorland, I felt sure that my superintendent would not authorize a prosecution under the Malicious Damage Act and told him that my recommendation would be 'no proceedings'. He thanked me, shook my hand and thanked me for saving his life. I told him I had not done so – for that, he must thank Jack Lewis and I gave him Jack's address.

On the way out, I saw John George's physician, Dr Handley, and asked for a word in private. In his office, I told him of John George's visit to Harley Street and to the doctor in Hull, whereupon Dr Handley frowned. He pulled a reference book off the shelf and asked, 'Who did he see about his heart trouble?'

I checked in my notebook and said, 'A Dr Brownlow, No. 19a.'

'There's no such person,' said Dr Handley. 'We have a list of all the Harley Street heart specialists . . . he's not there . . . see for yourself.'

'And what about the doctor in Hull?' I asked.

He made another check of his references and shook his head. 'No, no such person of that name either.'

'Have you examined him for heart or other problems?' I asked.

'Yes, we gave him a thorough medical once he'd come round. His heart's as sound as a bell, he's in real good health. And I'm sure I'd have spotted something if his liver or other organs were cancerous or causing problems.'

I then told Dr Handley about Yvonne Patricia Carlton-Kinross, the lady doctor who had come here on a specialist lecture tour and he said he knew nothing about it, but would check and ring me at home. I provided him with a list of some of the venues of her talks, as given to me by John George.

He rang me two days later.

'There's been no lecture tour by that Yvonne Patricia lady

doctor,' Dr Handley told me. 'No one in our profession's heard of her; some of us would have known the name, Constable, if she was a specialist over here from the States or wherever.'

'Do you think John George Crossfield has been conned good and proper?' I ventured to ask.

'I think he has,' laughed Dr Handley. 'After you'd gone the other day, I gave him another thorough going-over, heart, lungs, kidneys, the lot. I could find absolutely nothing wrong with him, he's a very fit man. Very fit indeed.'

'I wonder if she was a relation of one of his earlier victims?' I smiled. 'Getting her own back perhaps, in a very clever, feminine way. Hell hath no fury like a woman spurned and all that . . . .'

'He's had a fright,' Dr Handley said. 'Whatever she did to him, it's shaken his self-confidence. Now, he's over it all and I know he'll recover.'

'But will our moors recover?' I asked, realizing that some of our finest countryside had been devastated by the most recent of John George's man-made disasters.